PUT YOUR BEST VOICE FORWARD!

*DISCOVER hidden potential in your voice
*LEAD sales presentations
*WIN an audience
*TUNE IN to the voice messages from co-workers
*POWER speeches and sales presentations
*CONVINCE friends, family, and lovers . . .

with

VOICE POWER

EVELYN BURGE BOWLING is a speech pathologist and educational consultant for the Sunrise Language, Speech, and Educational Services. Previously she worked as a school speech and hearing therapist and as a private practitioner in remedial clinics.

VOICE POWER

BY
EVELYN
BURGE
BOWLING

ZEBRA BOOKS
KENSINGTON PUBLISHING CORP.

ZEBRA BOOKS

are published by

Kensington Publishing Corp.
475 Park Avenue South
New York, NY 10016

First Zebra Books printing: March 1986

Printed in the United States of America

To my aunt, Doris Hill,
whose loving friendship
and inspiring voice
have enriched my life

Contents

Acknowledgments

Simultaneously writing a book, running a business, managing a new home, and working with speech handicapped individuals has placed me in total gratitude to many people.

David Molinatto Koeth, my youngest old friend, is the graphic artist who designed the illustrations. David, who lives in Champion, Ohio, where I grew up and attended school, has shared an interest in art and owls with me since childhood.

My friend, Duane Newcomb initiated the book idea and prodded me in the planning stage. Gail Tucker, a fellow member of the American Association of University Women's Writers Group, Roseville branch, reviewed most of the manuscript and made many cogent suggestions.

From the other side of the country, John Crump guided me towards recent voice research, taught me to understand spectrograms, and provided information from the files at Kay Elemetrics in Pinebrook, New Jersey.

In the desert town of Cave Creek, Arizona, Edie Hennacy, whose friendship dates back to the first grade at Champion Township School, continuously supplied ideas and offered enthusiastic encouragement during the many months without weekend breaks. Another strong supporter in Roseville was Jean Briney, who collected tongue twisters and similes for chapter 8. Erma Emerson, Linda Briney, Betty Coyle, Payo Campean, and Peter Ogle made many helpful suggestions or developed publicity.

The arduous task of transcribing the entire first draft of the manuscript from my rambling and sometimes inaudible tapes fell to Traci Richter, a San Juan high school student. Traci also typed most of the chapters in the second draft preparing them for the final draft which was completed by Eunice Naber. Helping Eunice by proofing her work were the Bowling trio, Don, David, and Madge. They also took over many clinical and personal responsibilities to make it possible for me to write.

My thanks must also go to the numerous physicians, psychologists, scientists, voice teachers, and voice students who talked with me at the symposium on "Care of the Professional Voice" at the Julliard School, New York City, as well as those who shared ideas at other professional conferences during the year.

When I have used examples of individuals from my speech improvement classes, I have jumbled ages, sexes, occupations, and situations in order to protect privacy, unless I had specific permission to use their problem as an example. If you find yourself in my book in spite of all my revising tactics, I feel confident that you will be grateful for the inspiration, knowledge, and motivation your experience may give to someone in need.

Finally, I thank all of my clients for their under-standing, encouragement, and patience during the many months when I reduced the hours of my avail-ability at the clinic in order to immerse myself in this project. Without their inspiration, I would not have had the special joy possible only through writing a book and learning to accept the gracious help of caring friends.

Introduction

Your voice is the cutting edge of your personality with a language all its own which people recognize and respond to immediately. It can elicit a wide range of negative responses—irritation, rejection, even hatred. Or it can bring forth love, peace, happiness, and vibrant enthusiasm. Indeed, its unlimited possibilities make it your greatest tool.

It is never too late to develop a voice that will make an impact on your job and social relationships and open the door to a prosperous, more fulfilling life. However, very frequently people who do not like their voices are confused and frustrated when they seek help. Health and beauty classes, professional training, and even public speaking courses do not deal directly with voice. As their teachers are usually not trained in voice pathology, they cannot accurately identify problems, nor can they outline appropriate programs to correct them. Advice such as "speak as low as possible" can actually start a person on the road to a chronic voice problem.

On the other hand, most people do not need the intensive care of a professional speech pathologist who specializes in communicative disorders often caused by severe physical or emotional handicaps. The average person needs a program of *voice improvement*, which identifies special needs and matches them with relevant techniques that can be applied in daily life.

The exercises and advice in this book have been the foundation of success stories among those who learned them in my Voice Improvement Class. One very pretty student said, "I'm beginning to actually believe that men love to be seen with beautiful women, but seldom marry them. About the third time my last date suggested I needn't say a word, but just keep smiling, I wished I had fangs so I could punctuate my reaction!" The real problem was not that she was dull, but that she sounded like a chipmunk. We worked together to develop a pleasant, expressive voice through correcting pitch and timing.

Another person who was hiding the natural brilliance of his voice was a young lawyer plagued by his courtroom drone. He was thorough and precise in his work and always won his cases. Judges loved him, but he seldom had a satisfied client. He did not need to learn to use the dramatic pause or a fresh vocabulary or even to increase his loudness, and he certainly did not need the theatrical Perry Mason image that many judges resent. However, he had to inspire his clients' confidence; they wanted to hear the truth resound instead of trickle meekly out of the shuffle of papers. Voice power came when he learned to speak more slowly and clearly, open his mouth to let his resonance shine, and emphasize key words that left no doubt about his dauntless dedication to life, liberty, and the pursuit of victory in court.

One woman who would still insist that she is "just a housewife" earns far more than her husband through her dynamic use of voice as a representative for a vitamin company. She bought the products originally because her best friend sold them. Apparently they charged her with so much energy that she believed that she could do more than care for her husband and four young children.

"With your material, you could outsell Cosby, Diller, and Bombeck," I said after hearing how the baby's diaper had leaked on the dress of a visiting Methodist enthusiast, the two-year-old had nearly bitten off the finger of the Watkins Products man, the four-year-old had sat on the neighbor's rooster, and the six-year-old had had to be rescued from the top of the oak tree by the local fire department.

"I could never be a comedian. I'm just not the type," she replied. "I'm just thankful that now I have the energy to keep up with my kids. But really, I think I could sell those vitamins if I had more confidence before groups."

With a lesson a week, during the first month she began to expand both her voice skills and her confidence. When she had learned the basics, she tried practical assignments. She was to call all her friends and interest them in her intention to start a new career without actually revealing what this career would be. She used breathing, pitch, timing, resonance, and loudness to create suspense.

She was so convincing and humorous that she was obviously ready to practice face to face with strangers. Together, we went door to door to survey the frequency of the use of vitamin products. We evaluated the use of her voice after each encounter and returned to the clinic to play back tapes after visiting five houses. She progressed from faltering hesitancy to a warm, chatty style that allowed her to deviate from her script and comment on everything from the roses in the yard to whatever she spied beyond the doorway.

Still, she was aghast when I suggested she would soon be ready to telephone the president of the vitamin company in New York and convince him to hire her to start a branch business in her home, complete with a large consignment of the product. Most company presidents can spot competence and honesty and respond well to confidence. I had no doubt that she would succeed, and neither did she when three months later she was ready to make voice power her life-style.

Most people have no desire to change jobs when they join my class, but frequently they add new facets to their present jobs. In order to integrate your new image into your present life, it is very important to pin down personal ideals and the goals toward which you'll strive to realize them. One salesman who began with a guttural voice became a resonant baritone in just three weeks, then lost enthusiasm. When questioned about the halt in progress, he finally confided that his sales had increased so much in the three weeks that he was being considered for a promotion. This would mean a new sales territory, more time away from home and family, more responsibilities, and the fifth move in five years — all contrary to his ideal of warm, close family relationships.

The members of his voice class urged him to use his voice power to convince his supervisor that he could continue to develop his present territory. They suggested he ask the chamber of commerce about the new town, then convince his supervisor to take the new job. That way he could have his promotion and still remain in his present home. Not surprisingly, his natural pitch returned, as well as his ability to use pausing, phrasing, intensity, loudness, and resonance. His crisp pronounciation earned him the nickname "Richard Burton."

Eventually, his skills and confidence increased so much that he did want a new job that would allow fuller use of his voice. Because he was juggling his old job, the family, and the career change, he decided to seek help from a job development firm. His voice program had taught him to take responsibility for his health, wealth, and happiness, so he did not simply turn his career over to the firm. Voice power skills also meant a monetary savings to him, for he needed their services for two weeks, not three months. He avoided the downhill slide into depression that traps job-seekers who lack voice power.

To improve your voice most successfully, constantly keep in mind your personal ideals and goals. For the best results in the shortest time with this book, write down an ideal for every chapter. Read it over aloud in a determined voice, and then put it with your valuable papers. Close your eyes and picture yourself acting the way you chose as your ideal. The more detailed your imagination of this scene is, the stronger the impression will be. Sometimes it helps to draw stick figures of yourself acting out your ideals.

Through voice power, people become more aware not just of their own beliefs and actions, but also those of others. For example, a tired, depressed voice;

hoarseness; or facial and neck tension are signals that alert you to approaching changes in others' dispositions. Recognizing them before a disagreement enables you to help someone retain composure or regain it even after pelting you with angry or sarcastic gibes.

Responsible use of voice guides you toward becoming the person you've dreamed of being. Letting your mental, physical, and spiritual ideals be the yardstick for all your decisions is the key to attaining that goal. Bringing out the fullest potential of your voice will allow you to share your best through the beautiful, expressive channel of your individually creative voice.

ONE

Identifying
What's Wrong with
Your Voice

In the 1920s, thousands flocked to see John Gilbert on the silver screen. He was handsome, dashing, and sophisticated, and he stole the heart of every woman in the audience as he made love to Greta Garbo. Then came the talkies, and he was ruined, for John Gilbert had a high-pitched voice, and that didn't fit the role of the masculine matinee idol.

The story of actors of the twenties who faded into oblivion with the advent of sound in films is an extreme example of how the lack of an effective voice can lead to failure. Unfortunately, most people do not equate their own need for voice power with the needs of those of celluloid fame. That can be a drastic mistake. Voice contributes as much to a total image as physical appearance, poise, and personality, and vocal habits can detract from an otherwise positive and command- ing social presence. A strong voice draws attention and a weak one does not, even if what it has to say is quite profound.

Fortunately, effective voice habits are as easy to learn as habits of poise and social grace, and once mastered, they can be a tool to achieving success in business and satisfaction in personal relationships.

All that is needed is desire, time, and some simple techniques in voice improvement. This book will aid you by providing a variety of special exercises which, if followed carefully, will open the door to voice power, the best use of your voice.

The first step is to determine the exact nature of your voice habits by becoming acquainted with the way you really sound. You'll need a couple of five-by-seven-inch pieces of cardboard. Place the five-inch edge of the cardboard firmly on the bones in front of your ears so that it extends out from the side of your head. Read the following paragraph in a loud voice:

> Your voice is the cutting edge of your personality, with a language all its own, which people recognize and respond to immediately. It can elicit a wide range of responses. Irritation, rejection, downright hate. On the other hand, it can bring forth acceptance, happiness, joy, and unbridled enthusiasm. In short, your voice is a personality tool with almost unlimited possibilities.

Now put down the cardboard and read the passage again, cupping your ears. You should notice a distinct difference. The use of the cardboard demonstrates how your voice sounds to others. Cupping your ears exaggerates what you usually perceive as your own voice. Most people are surprised and disappointed when they hear their voice on tape and often don't believe that the recorder is accurately reflecting their voice quality. Be aware that you don't sound the same way to others as you do to yourself.

Next, hold up the cardboard once again and look into a mirror. Pucker your lips while keeping as small an opening as possible and say, "How are you today? I'm just fine." You will notice that you change the resonance, or the amplification, of your voice. Resonance is created by the vibration of the sounds of the voice through eighteen different structures, from the base of the rib cage up. The pucker test helped you find a resonance quality focused in the back of your mouth. Of course there are other places to focus your voice. Music teachers say that the area used to create resonance differentiates the good singer from the poor one, and that's also true in speech. For good resonance, you must learn to control the placement of sound in your oral cavity and consistently choose the location of your best sounding voice.

Very often, after the above test, some people complain that they sound unnatural. This frequently comes from the nasal speaker. Nasality is the most common resonance problem in the United States. To find out if you're nasal, put your fingers on the bridge of your nose and say, "A, E, I, O, U." If you felt any vibration, you are probably a nasal speaker. Only the French language has nasalized vowels. All the English vowels are supposed to be produced in various parts of the mouth.

You can probably name five people that you know with voice problems. They include people whose voices are too low or too high, too soft or too loud. Others speak so fast they can't be understood or so slowly that they are boring. It is important at this stage to find out how others perceive your voice. Find several friends or

21

acquaintances you feel you can trust to be honest and not overly concerned about hurting your feelings. Make copies of the following questionnaire and ask your selected critics to fill them out and return them to you. Don't worry if you run across a person who ridicules you and exaggerates your problems on the answer sheet. Just disregard it. Do, however, encourage your critics to be as complete as possible in their formation of the sound picture you will use to evaluate your voice.

❦

PERSONAL VOICE QUESTIONNAIRE

Please check all the numbers in each category that describe _____'s voice. These results are critical for a voice study project. Evaluators were selected on the basis of sensitivity, objectivity, and familiarity with the voice of the subject. Use (?) to indicate when choices are not firm.

VOICE QUALITY	LOUDNESS	TIMING
1. Breathy	1. Quiet	1. Smooth
2. Raspy	2. Loud	2. Jerky, stuttering
3. Warm	3. Confidential	3. Fast, frequent, fluent
4. Enthusiastic	4. Soft	4. Slow, plodding
5. Icy	5. Penetrating	5. Varied, exciting
6. Dignified	6. Inaudible	6. Deliberate, authoritative
7. Clear	7. Vibrant	7. Inadequate pausing
8. Scratchy	8. Monotonous	8. Hesitant, "and-uhs"
9. Sultry	9. Dynamic	9. Drawl, foreign accent

| | 10. Lifeless | 10. Variable | 10. Unvaried |

PITCH	RESONANCE	ARTICULATION, WORD USAGE
1. Squeaky	1. Nasal	1. Crisp, fresh, dynamic
2. Guttural	2. Hollow	2. Slushy
3. Shrill	3. Twangy	3. Lispy
4. Flat	4. Mouthy	4. Mumbled
5. Unvaried	5. Denasal	5. Frequent stale expressions
6. Low	6. Mellow	6. "R" or "I" distortions
7. Masculine	7. Muffled	7. Slighted "ing" endings
8. Effeminate	8. Whiney	8. Slangy
9. Childish	9. Unremarkable	9. Regional distortions
10. Pleasing	10. Throaty	10. Dull vocabulary

The questionnaire has probably motivated you to wonder why many of the descriptions were applied to you. You can't change something about your voice until you know exactly where the trouble is. Since others may determine much of what happens in your life, keep in mind what they think of your voice.

Voice differences become more apparent when concentrated on the telephone. Some people's telephone voices cause you to hold the receiver about six inches from your ear. There are others to whom you consistently say "could you speak a little louder," or "a little slower," or "please repeat that." A telephone survey for voice analysis will help you identify more about your voice and how it is perceived by listeners. For some people the telephone survey is easier than handing out questionnaires. You need not meet anyone face to face, and they'll never know your identity. Since today is the era of telephone surveys, most people are willing to cooperate when you state that you are conducting a survey. Most people you reach will never have been contacted by a survey representative and therefore have been skeptical of the results of published polls. They will be pleased and satisfied by your call and will cooperate with your request.

Take a few minutes before beginning this project to attain the right frame of mind. You want to be systematic and totally objective. You have absolutely nothing to fear. The worst that could happen would be someone hanging up or refusing to answer questions. If that happens, simply go to the next number. Out of the twenty numbers that you select first, more than ten of them will be cooperative and helpful.

Write down your list of numbers on a lined sheet of paper leaving space for recording the responses. It's best to have one sheet of paper for each number and several alternate numbers listed after the original choice. Some of my students have enjoyed making a game out of selecting the numbers. For example, they have chosen names such as Jones, Smith, or Turner, or an unusual name like Zickenfouse, and then have telephoned all of the numbers listed for that name. Others have picked names with eight letters in the surname, or names beginning with the letter Q, while others simply take a straight pin, close their eyes, touch the point on the directory page, and call the name it touches.

Your method of selection can be individualistic, but

for good results, do not vary the procedure after dialing. Dial the number and say:

I am doing an information survey to find out how people react to various kinds of voices. Your number has been selected and I would appreciate your answering these questions. First, can you hear me clearly? All right then, you're ready for the questions. They will take only two minutes of your time. Here is question number one. (Never say you want their help because it may motivate sympathy, a refusal, or a personal discussion.)

1. Can you detect any foreign accent in my voice?
2. Can you guess what part of the country I am from?
3. Please estimate how many years of school I've had from the way I speak: eight years, twelve years, fourteen years, or sixteen years.
4. Would you rate my voice as:
   a. Unclear
   b. Acceptable
   c. Average
   d. Colorful
   e. Dynamic
5. You have been listening to my voice now for about one minute. To your ear, would I sound better if my voice were on a lower pitch or a higher pitch?

Thank you for your answers. Your comments are exactly the kind needed for this study. Goodbye.

Hang up quickly or you may find yourself in a conversation that takes too much time. If you run across someone who interrupts with a great many questions, just hang up and go on to the next number. The purpose is not conversation but information. Compulsive questioners often are of little help, as they spend so much time weighing the questions that it is doubtful whether they really have any firm opinions.

The telephone survey is an adventure, and the results are usually intriguing. For example, if you are rated as having a foreign accent, you can be sure that many of your vowels and some of your consonants are incorrectly produced. In my opinion, foreign accents often add a charm, warmth, and distinction to a person's voice. However, if it frequently interferes with communication and understandability, you do have a problem! In any case, if you are consistently asked to repeat what you have just carefully explained, your articulation needs improvement. Clearing up the consonant sounds may be the little bit of change needed for understandable speech. The vowel sounds can be that bit of difference needed to identify you with the special background you want to retain, as it does the Southerner. However, if you were not raised in the South and are guessed frequently to be Southern, you're probably mangling many vowel sounds. Maybe this adds charm to your voice, but if it interferes with talking to people from other parts of the country or prohibits you from obtaining a job you would like to have, then you've got work to do.

If the people guessed you were from New Jersey and New York, you may be consistently distorting the "r" sound as well as shortening certain vowel sounds. Your speech may also be too rapid. As much as we'd like to believe these patterns have no impact on hiring or in choosing relationships, the evidence is to the contrary. A few weeks ago, I overheard the following comment about a friend of mine. "I know she has a college education, but I would never guess it from the way she talks. Can you imagine her as a receptionist in a speech clinic?" There was much laughter and then, "Isn't it sad that not one of us would ever have the courage to tell her about her speech?" The sound this young woman misused was "r" and it was distorted or omitted in most of her words. "Dirty" became "doity" and "thirty" became "thoity." The "r" was added in some instances to the ends of words creating "bananers" and "Cubar." Like most people she never realized how different she sounded.

Regional accents may contribute to an individualistic voice, but they often cause the speaker to be judged as uneducated, dull, or boring. The listener believes the inadequacy is in the person rather than in the voice. It is not unusual to meet brilliant people who really have much to offer but who speak in such monotonous tones that it is difficult to pay attention to what they have to say.

If you were rated as having an average voice in the survey, I'm sorry to say that your critic probably really meant dull but was too kind to use the label. Dullness for the average voice usually means not changing speech rate, loudness, intensity, or voice pitch. The most trivial incident can be made exciting by varied use of these elements. Since quite a bit of our daily conversation is about trivia, it makes sense to learn to speak in a lively manner.

The answers to the questions about pitch in the survey probably do not pertain to your own voice but reflect a general consensus that lower pitches are preferred to higher-pitched voices. If you, for example, were said to have nasal speech, your pitch is higher than it should be. You simply cannot produce a low-pitched nasal voice! The most complained about voices are in the higher range, and you'll learn to handle that problem in chapter 3.

A rate that is too fast usually accompanies a higher voice. Speed seems to be the watchword for our present technological generation, and this is often reflected in speech. It's as though everyone were in a big rush. Leisurely communication is the exception rather than the rule. Why not take time to smell the flowers along the way, or in other words, why not take time to savor your speech and enjoy communicating with the marvelous tools of language that you have — your words and your voice?

So far, you still do not have any information on your breathing, your tension spots, and the way that you use your body to communicate. A furrowed brow, lifted eyebrows, a strained neck, or a slouched posture can have an influence on your voice production. Using a full-length mirror and the following exercises, you will be able to identify patterns that you have developed over the years.

Tension is often the source of muscle patterns you'll want to eliminate. Seated in front of the mirror, you will be able to pinpoint exactly where the problems occur and how your breath and body contribute to their creation. Just as the tape recorder can tell whether or not there is melody or monotony in your voice, your mirror can reflect muscle tension patterns on your face and body. Watch yourself now as you repeat the following phrases and sentences. Be sure to look directly into your own eyes as you say them. Pretend these are relevant to your life.

1. Have you noticed that Mother is always complaining or criticizing?
2. I misplaced my car keys again. Did you see them?
3. I wish she would take the kids' trash out of the car after she uses it.
   Did you notice where I put my wallet? I just can't find it.
   From the racket in here, I don't think you know how to turn down the volume.

Did some lines in your face deepen when you read at least one of those sentences? A line can form only when the muscles are required to work the same way many, many times a day. Lines are usually a clear sign of intense stress in the facial and throat areas during speaking or listening. Of course, smile lines around the eyes and the corners of the mouth would tell a different story, but, unfortunately, not many people have joy lines imprinted upon their faces.

Posture also plays a part in the amount of stress experienced during listening and speaking. When humans adopted the upright posture, apparently a large majority abstained from the vote. The casual slouch is not just popular among the teenage population. In fact, with the emphasis today upon physical fitness in our schools, the average teenager may have better posture than most of the adults you see on the street. Since many of us sit at desk jobs throughout the day or stand on our feet doing something with our hands, we are likely to become accustomed to postures that are not healthy or helpful to voice. Not only does voice quality suffer because of poor posture, but vital organs may also reap the effect of a crunched position during waking hours. Circulation is lessened, and the organs' waste products, when not carried away efficiently, turn into digestive problems as well as diseases.

Good posture certainly is not the military form often thought of when someone says to stand up straight. I'll explain how to maintain a vigilance over your posture in the next chapter. It's an ongoing process, but one that will certainly improve your health and vitality as well as your attitude about many things. And since attitude is so very important, I will begin now with the most basic ingredient for voice — your breath. So, take a deep one and start thinking about your breath and your body in the creation of your true, full, voice power.

TWO

Creating Voice Power with Your Breath and Body

Voice power is not energy that just comes from the throat. It is created by the entire body. How the body is cared for has much to do with the development of voice power, voice image, and the imprint that the voice leaves on others.

The body reflects the care that is given it. Many times body language becomes voice language. It is rare to find a great voice emanating from a sickly, cadaverous body. However, it is possible for someone with a very small physical body to develop a voice power that influences the world. The many famous and infamous people of small stature whose voices will live in history forever derived their voice power from an intense sense of purpose and supported it with continuous energy.

That energy was generated from the efficient functioning of at least four of the major body processes — circulation, assimilation, rest, and elimination. It is essential to ensure that these four processes work at peak condition at all times. Although they seem to happen without doing anything, it is important to understand that development of maximum efficiency only comes from daily attention.

Good circulation requires an exercise program that uses breathing to its fullest limits. For many, a daily exercise program helps the other three body-go-powers keep right on target. It is important for everyone to engage in some kind of regular exercise regimen. With good circulation from physical activities, digestion is improved, along with the body's ability to assimilate food. Then the muscles demand rest, sleep is sound, and the fourth body process, elimination, is taken care of through the skin, lungs, bowels, and bladder. Of course, elimination is a key to care of the total body. If the eliminating organs don't work, death occurs. The body must get rid of the waste products it continuously creates as it functions. Fresh fruit, grains, and vegetables as part of a sound nutritional program assist and stimulate elimination.

The degree to which these four bodily functions work well determines the degree of health, and only with a healthy body can you consistently feel well, live well, and do well. Start with just three daily habits to help you achieve the efficient functioning of the body processes and augment them with nutrition and exercise programs so that you will enjoy the most benefit from your efforts.

1. Drink two or more quarts of good water. If you dislike drinking water as much as I do, try adding a blop of lemon juice. If it still repels you, add a bit of honey. Your body is more than 95 percent water, and it really needs to be changed often. I am particular about my water and buy only purified. I believe that since the body is mostly water and must have it to function, I'll tip the scales in my favor by buying the best I can.

Since I dislike drinking water so much, I really must practice the habit or I soon conveniently forget it. I drink two full glasses immediately upon waking up. Sometimes I set the glasses on my bed stand so that I won't be fully awake and completely resistant when I drink it.

I guzzle two more glasses before noon and set out two more glasses for the afternoon. Honestly, drinking water is one of the hardest caring-for-my-body techniques I use, and I hope *you* won't find it so difficult.

Nothing else counts as water — coffee, tea, herb teas, carrot juice, wine, beer, and milk don't count. They may be drunk in addition to the water, but it's really difficult to keep track of all you drink besides water — so don't. Just be sure you drink your water quota. Of course, you can find hundreds of authorities who will agree with me and hundreds more who won't. The only way to know if I'm correct about the body's needs for lots of good water is to try it yourself for at least a week. If you don't feel better, I'm wrong!

2. More water. This time, on your body to help your skin with its trillions of pores do its work of elimination. I personally feel that sitting in a tub of warm water allows it to gently soak into little holes in your skin and float out some of the debris. We are a nation of shower lovers with lots of soap. To many, it would be blasphemy to suggest that this procedure isn't the greatest for a total body care program. However, this time, try joining the minority opinion of some healthbook writers who say we soap off our natural oil too efficiently. With it goes part of our immunity system and we open the door to bothersome colds and infections, and perhaps add wrinkles earlier. Soap is

great in the right places in the right amount, but the skin has a problem maintaining the needed germ-fighting acidity when it is alkalized daily with too much soap. The skin breathes and reacts to what is in the air.

So do the lungs. I wish I could recommend clean air as part of your total body care for voice power, but this seems to become less practical every day. I just heard a story of a doctor administering artificial respiration to an accident victim on one of our city streets. He chanted as he pushed, "Out goes the bad air, in goes the bad air."

But whether the air is good or bad, breathing habits radically affect voice power. Good breathing supports good voice quality, builds resonance, and makes it possible to increase loudness without strain. It doesn't come from heaving your shoulders up and down.

It does come from pushing your stomach in and out. With lips closed, breathe rapidly through your nose. Do it as fast as you can to feel what I'm talking about. When you took a breath in, your stomach came out. When you released it, your stomach went in. Unfortunately many people go through the entire day without ever taking one complete breath—taking in as much air as possible and then letting it completely out. It's one of the best treats for the lungs, not to mention all the other body parts that require oxygen to help keep you alive. It is not really hard to develop if you "sniff up" air. And that's what we'll learn to do in number three.

3. Learn to completely fill your lungs every day. You can remain seated if you wish, but I'd suggest you put your back flat against the wall for the best start. Facing a full-length mirror is even better. Then you can

actually see what you feel.

With lips pressed together, begin to take short, quick sniffs through your nose. Keep sniffing until you can't get any more air into your lungs. Your chest will expand and rise. You have put air into every space available and completely filled the tiny air sacs in your lungs. The stomach muscles have worked to the fullest, too. Now release the air, pulling in your stomach as far as it will go. Help it with your hands to get all of the air out. Repeat the procedure, but this time, work harder.

When you have sniffed up as much air as possible, hold it, with your stomach protruding way out, until you have silently and slowly counted to ten. Now release, pulling your stomach way in, and silently count to four while holding the air out of your body. When you can do that, you've begun to take control of your breath power. If you can manage as many as sixteen short sniffs to fill your lungs, you've reached the top for most people, but there are show-offs who can take as many as twenty-five short sniffs, and that's really control!

Another exercise is to stand with your feet about six inches apart. Inhale very slowly as you gradually raise your arms from your sides and your heels off the floor. When your arms are shoulder level, pull your shoulders back as far as they will go. Continue inhaling and raising your arms until your hands meet overhead. Complete your breath and hold it while counting to four. This strengthens the muscles and, according to one yoga teacher, gives the blood a chance to take in oxygen. Now reverse the process.

Slowly bring your arms down as you exhale. Your heels are gradually lowered to the floor. Pull your stomach in as far as it will go and hold the breath out of your body while you count to four again. Now you are ready to repeat the entire process. Two complete breaths are better than one, and three will give you even more benefits. Did you have a sense of control as you released your breath or did it get away from you and gush out?

If you exhaled too quickly the first time, work for control. Try counting silently to sixteen as you exhale. Some students actually made it to twenty-five. Try holding the breath out for a count to ten but don't push yourself too hard. Remember you are striving for control, not endurance. People who have had strokes, surgery, or other physical problems require a different individualized approach, and although they can accomplish a great deal on their own, they should work with a speech professional who will show them a variety of specific techniques for special problems.

One of the fringe benefits that comes with breath control is posture improvement. Good posture is essential for breathing better, looking better, and tiring less. If you sit on your "sitting bones," your spine will be aligned and your posture perfect. With the intake of air, the chest lifts and the shoulders come into line with the hips. That's the exact carriage needed for the full expression of a dynamic person. Slouching causes a health problem from muscle tensions, pressures of bones against soft tissue, and poor circulation in the compressed chest area. Try sniffing in air in a super-slouched position with your elbows on your lap to feel how incompatible a slouch is with breathing.

To make sure you are sitting properly, before you sit, feel the back of your legs touch the front of the chair.

Then sit straight down on those two bones that you feel make contact with the chair. If you can, don't use your hands and make your back muscles work. You can take a deep breath as you begin to sit and exhale when your bones meet the chair. If you consciously take a deep breath whenever you sit, you'll constantly get good breathing practice.

The next step in learning breath control is to sniff in air again and say "ho, ho, ho," quickly and briskly until you run out of breath. Feel your stomach muscles learning to work for you. Also feel the release of tension—the number one antagonist to good voice quality. Tension is often a pain in the neck, and I mean that literally. Stiffness and tightness often collect in the head, neck, and upper chest. If you make your neck and jaw as tight as possible, clench your teeth, and try to say, "Today is the best day of my life," you'll feel that it isn't! When you hear a voice that makes you pull back and turn off, you can be sure that the muscles are squeezed somewhere. The bigger the squeeze, the stranger the voice. The best way to start loosening up is to give the shoulders a roll.

To do that, make two fists. Then, keeping your upper arms at your sides, bend your elbow and hold your fists out in front of you. Raise your shoulders high and move your elbows backward. Then bring your shoulders and elbows down. The movement is like the piston action of the old steam engine. Continue for ten repetitions and notice what happens. The air is forced out of your body as you bring your shoulders down. If you didn't start with a deep breath, sniff in air through your nose and let it out through your mouth with a loud "ha" as your elbows and shoulders press down.

This develops strength in your sound-making muscles as well as giving you a head start on improving voice quality.

That "ha" sound is one of the hallmarks of a pleasant quality. You have to open your mouth to make it and most of us talk so rapidly we don't. Practice the shoulder roll a few more times and this time say "jot," "bought," "caught," "forgot," "dot," "blot," and "not" when you bring your shoulders down.

You may feel some discomfort when you move your shoulders. Now try moving your head sideways from shoulder to shoulder. The sounds, pains, and ache are gentle reminders that you need daily work in this area. Rolling your head is a good starter—back three times, to the left three times, forward three times, and to the right three times. Be sure to take your time and concentrate on feeling the muscles work. Keeping your eyes open during this movement can actually improve eyesight for a few moments, through the subtle relaxation of the eye muscles. Look at a page of print (take your glasses off if you wear them), slowly and carefully repeat this exercise three times, with open eyes and then look at the page again. It will be clearer for a few moments as a result of the relaxation. The relaxation effect usually immediately affects the voice quality, too. Cup your ears and say, "I am sounding unusually good today." The stretching movement temporarily stops the stress in the jaws, lips, vocal folds, as well as the neck. If you literally keep a stiff upper lip, you'll be stiff-necked, too, and the voice won't be the best you. You can hear your voice improve as you repeat the head and neck exercise adding some sound.

Say "oh, oh, oh" as you slowly drop the head

forward. Repeat "ooo" (as in moon) three times as the head goes to the left. Do "ah" three times as the head stretches backward, "ee" three times as the head bends to the right, and "oh" again as it is lowered forward. By adding the sounds, you heard less of your cracking neck and of the foggy or scratchy sound in your voice if that's one of your problems now. You relaxed your neck and made a giant step forward toward producing high quality vowel sounds, and a completely relaxed body will move you even closer to that goal.

Of course, it is hard to be consistently relaxed all day through, but the trick is to find techniques that will work to balance the tension that is bound to accumulate in parts of your body each day. One technique I learned from a seventy-five-year-old man with a beautiful, youthful voice involves spine stretching. When I asked how he kept his beautiful voice, he replied, "I hang myself once a day." Then he showed me a gadget of ropes attached to a cloth band and a pulley. He hooked one rope to the top of a door casing, put his chin in the band, and pulled the rope. Slowly his chin was raised up as high as possible and then lowered through releasing the rope slowly. His eyes twinkled as he watched mine widen with concern.

"Don't you know that all your nerves branch off your spine?" he asked. "I figure if you keep your spine in good condition, you'll probably keep the rest of your body tip-top too." I readily admitted that the stretching in the neck probably did have a part in retaining his voice and began to check other sources to see if a flexible spinal column had any relation to total body health. It does.

Rather than hanging yourself daily, try this. Lie on

the floor, clasp your hands around your knees, rock backward as far as you can, and then rock forward. A bit strenuous, but helpful in maintaining the body in good physical condition. If you add practice with the vowel sounds, "oh, ee, ah, oo," you will be on your way to more flexible lips and jaw and better diction as you limber up your spine. One blooming student of mine with a blossoming behind insisted that this rocking exercise also bumped away a few inches.

She contributed another exercise to keep the spine flexible. She found she could do it without getting out of bed and it helped her to wake up in the morning.

Begin flat on your back. Bend your knees, keeping feet flat on the bed or floor. Fold your hands and put them under your head. Move your knees closely together to the right touching the floor. Then move them to the left touching the floor. Feel a pull in your waistline? A fringe benefit from doing one hundred a day is pulling in your belt another two notches. Twenty a day should keep the spine flexible and won't be quite so hard on your sitting bones either.

Sometimes, even with these daily exercises, you really don't realize how hard you hang on to tension until you suddenly let go. That complete release doesn't happen often to most of us. Instead, we let go a little at a time till finally we are totally relaxed, perhaps over a period of hours. But there's a quicker way to achieve the "Total Let Go."

Tighten your whole body—jaws, fists, neck, knees, toes—and count slowly to ten. Now release just fingers. Then your arms. Now your jaws and your neck. Finally your knees and legs and last, uncurl your toes. It will feel great as the strain leaves your muscles. It's almost as if you took your muscles out of a straitjacket and floated them in air!

Awareness of tension is the first step to its total control. If you do your tension practice frequently, you will learn to monitor your whole tension theme. You'll be able to notice that certain muscles are contracted and will be able to decontract them before disaster sets in. For some, disaster is the pain in the neck; for others, a tension headache; and for thousands of others, irritability and a very short temper. And, of course, the voice communicates all of this too clearly.

Each time you care for your precious body by stopping the buildup of tension, you contribute to everyone's relaxation. And there's good reason for wanting to do that; it could save your life. Instead of wanting revenge on the truck driver who climbs up your back on the highway and then cuts in front of you, you can let that angry tension go. After you've been criticized, nagged, and can't find your keys, you can let go instead of bellowing at the nearest body. Just your effort not to add to the daily frenzy of people rubbing each other the wrong way will begin to cause a ripple on the sea of unrest around you. It takes at least two to make a conflict, but the decision on the part of just one can change the lives of every person who is in contact with that changer, or should I say charger! Actually, many relaxation techniques are chargers.

This may sound strange to you, but here's how it works. When you become serenely in charge of the direction of your energy, you achieve more because you are goal-directed. Instead of using precious power to stumble around, lose things, blame, complain, and defend yourself, you direct that energy right to the task

41

at hand. It gets done. You feel accomplishment. You give yourself the needed pat. You go on to do more of the things that are really important to you rather than the garbage that is time-consuming, anxiety producing, and mind seducing.

The mass media tries to seduce us into believing we are victims who must constantly fight to get ahead. The excitement of believing it and the adventure of doing it are vividly portrayed. Fortunately we all know deeply that this isn't our true nature. You can escape this mentality if you learn some mind-relaxing techniques and practice them along with the body-relaxing ones.

Try this: rub the palms of your hands together briskly until you build up some heat. Now place your palms directly over your eyes. Let your fingers cross and rest on your forehead. Your elbows should rest on a stiff pillow or a table. Now start saying all the simple words beginning with "A." When you run out of "A" words, go on to "B," then "C." Continue down the alphabet. Don't struggle to find words and don't think about the meaning of words. Just let them flow without strain. If you can think of only two words for each letter, that's plenty.

What did you accomplish by that? So much that I probably don't have enough physiological and psychological terms to identify each specific accomplishment. but first and foremost, you did relax your body and your mind by cutting out 85 percent of your total stimulation.

You cut out stimulation by eliminating seeing, your main information source. By trapping your mind into focusing on one continuous activity — simple word finding and repetition — you eliminated worry and regret about other people. You also stopped thinking about the task in which you were previously involved, giving that set of facts and information a chance to regroup in your brain. You demonstrated to yourself that you can control your thoughts.

That is a powerfully important demonstration because most of us experience a lack of thought control during most of our waking day. Painful, annoying reminders of people, physical problems, and past mistakes flash in and out as we work, study, read, and relate to others. Everything we have ever done is stored in our complex brain, and it constantly spurts out relevant and irrelevant stuff, often hindering rather than helping. While you had your palms over your eyes and were focused on one specific, simple naming task, you made an inroad toward shutting off distractions. You stopped your mind-seeing as well as your eye-seeing.

Some currently popular therapy procedures, however, can damage the voice. Therapies involving intensive screaming or weightlifting with grunting may relax a person, but the side effects include vocal abuse. I frequently teach massaging the ear lobes, brushing the lymphatic areas, massaging the feet, or singing to assist those who complain they fall asleep during evening movies, lectures, or classes, or simply run out of energy long before they've completed tasks they had planned.

Since more than 200 acupuncture points are located on the ears, the energy flow to the part of the body the point is related to can be improved without using needles. One Western explanation interprets acupuncture points as places in the body's electrical system that are close to the surface and respond easily to stimulation. My method involves gently massaging the entire lobe. This can be done while leaning on one elbow, unnoticed by anyone else. Some authorities say sleep may result if the pressure is firm. I find the ear lobes become invigoratingly warm in addition to bringing back energy.

Stimulating the lymphatic system located near the surface of the body has been one of the most productive techniques for many of my students. The lymph system carries away impurities. A gentle brush with your fingertips refreshes, relaxes, and discourages the tension buildup that brings edginess and strain into your body and is always reflected in your voice. You must not use a heavy hand, because the lymph system's fluids do not work well when moving rapidly.

Begin by using the fingertips of your right hand to lightly brush from the inside of your left elbow to under your armpit fifty or more times. Repeat on your right arm using your left fingertips. Switch hands and brush down the left side of your neck and off your shoulder. Change hands and do the other side. Now using both hands, brush up your front from your waistline. Continue to use the fifty light strokes as you brush up the opposite area on your back. The last lymph area to stimulate is on your inside thighs of both legs. As you brush this final area, keep the touch light, especially if your tissue is delicate. I was once over-energetic and produced a few bruises. It was difficult convincing the bathing suit crowd that I did it myself!

Foot massages have gained popularity with the rediscovery of ancient knowledge delineating the places on the feet that stimulate many organs throughout the body. Reflexologists and other health practitioners, who massage feet with various instruments, point to an impressive body of information purporting to identify specific areas for healing certain conditions. Although I personally have not experienced verification of any of the healing claims, I have found that systematic stimulation of the palms of the hands or the bottoms of the feet can produce energizing effects throughout the body, because both have more nerve endings than any other body parts. Push and rotate the eraser tip of a pencil in small circles to deeply massage every area of the sole, arch, heel, toes, and ankles. This will produce increased energy in the neck, head, stomach, back, and other areas that tighten under tension. I do this when riding in the back seat of a car on my way to lectures in distant cities. It certainly counteracts the effects of the traffic, the confinement of the car, and the slow passage of time, and I arrive fresh and ready to be at my best on the platform.

Although wailing, moaning, groaning, and screaming have also become popular therapies for tension release, I am not convinced that over time they do anything beneficial. They may actually reinforce patterns of complaining that have been active in an individual's behavior for years. When I am asked about these often expensive approaches, I recommend instead that the student take singing lessons. Most insist they could never learn to sing, don't have a "good voice," and would feel uncomfortable even trying to develop one. There is plenty of evidence that these are all myths.

Literally anyone can express himself by learning to

control his voice. Only a very few people are actually tone deaf. So far I have not encountered one person whom I could not teach to vary pitch, and all of the music teachers and voice scientists I have interviewed tell me that this agrees with their research and experience.

The modern voice teacher is excited about opening up good singing techniques for everyone and does not push all students toward a performance career. The percentage of people who can ever support themselves through vocal performance is very small, but the opportunities to enjoy participating in music and experience harmony of mind, body, and spirit are unlimited. Ancient records are filled with accounts of singing used in healing, and modern music therapists have an abundance of data to show the effectiveness of song therapy.

The new philosophy of teaching singing stresses the individuality of each voice and does not attempt to duplicate a voice model that exists in the mind of the music teacher or a vocal text. One voice teacher, Jeanette Queen, conducts vocal workshops in New York City to help people develop an individualistic voice and style to express their attitudes and feelings. Jeanette said that all students are asked to spend some time thinking about what part of them they want to express with their singing voices. Singing, according to this method, is another way of regaining the balance that is frequently easily lost with the current life-styles.

The costs may be a pleasant surprise. A voice studio I now use gives four individual lessons a month for twenty-eight dollars. Three other voice teachers I queried quoted from five to seven dollars for a half-hour lesson. When working with the delicate muscles of the vocal folds, knowledgeable teachers do not suggest a longer lesson for a beginning student.

Since your voice is affected by the entire body, take a good look at your health in general. According to Dr. Norman Shealey, 90 percent of today's health problems are caused by life-style. Dr. Shealey, a physician, neurosurgeon, and psychologist with thirty years of experience in these three fields, set up the first clinic for the treatment of chronic pain, which now rarely uses surgery or drugs. An author as well as president of the Holistic Health Medical Association, Dr. Shealey devotes a portion of his time to teaching well people how to bolster their present health and prevent disease, aging, and stress from diminishing their lifespans. Adequate physical exercise, good nutrition, and proper mental self-regulation, including will and attitude, are part of the life-style he stresses. Here are his ten commandments for good health:

1. Eat three meals a day, minimizing sugar and including a wide variety of foods.
2. Eat breakfast every day and start the day with adequate protein.
3. Do not smoke. It impedes cell oxygenation; hinders absorption of amino acids; and damages heart, lungs, and nerve tissue.
4. Do not drink, or if you do, minimize alcohol in your diet with a maximum of two ounces of whiskey, two beers, or two glasses of wine in a twenty-four-hour period.
5. Exercise hard enough to double the heart beat. Start off with one or two minutes and build up to a

one-hour goal each week over a period of six months.

6. Keep your weight within 10 percent of your ideal. People who are more than 10 percent overweight or underweight do not live as long and are not as healthy.
7. Sleep seven or eight hours each night.
8. Relax ten minutes, preferably three times a day. Certainly relax thirty minutes throughout a given day.
9. Never go to bed with a grudge inside you or beside you. Resolve your anger and fear each day.
10. Have faith in yourself.

All of Dr. Shealey's ideas complement the concept of creating voice power with your breath and your body. Part of the balance maintained this way is reflected in the pitch of your voice. The next chapter will guide you toward finding your natural pitch, the appropriate pitch that will serve as a foundation for your voice development.

THREE

Voice Power
Begins with
Natural Pitch

The effect of inappropriate pitch is often much more damaging than its producer realizes. An irritating pitch implies specific undesirable character traits. For example, a person speaking far above his or her natural pitch may be thought to be someone with an abrasive personality, rather than merely someone who has a bad voice habit. People tend to tune out an irritating voice, even if what is being said is interesting and worthwhile. Understandably, they avoid social contacts with persons whose voices grate on the ears and jangle their nerves.

I well remember one unfortunate man referred to me by a psychologist who complained that immediately after meeting strangers, they made it quite obvious that they couldn't wait to get away from him. The psychologist told me: "I can't do a thing for that screechy voice. It drives everyone up the wall."

Voice range or pitch problems are often developed during the teenage years, a time complicated by the stress of growing up. We have difficulty judging our own voices because of the location of ears, the distor-

49

tion caused by the bones in the head, and the position of the voice-producing muscles. The belief that voice changes are a natural process of maturation results in even unpleasant developments being ignored.

The most obvious problem is a voice that is extremely high or harshly low. Neither of these creates the warm, positive image inherent in your natural pitch.

In this chapter the first focus will be on discovering whether your habitual pitch is really your natural pitch and on helping you to find your appropriate speaking level. Even if you are one of the fortunate who already speaks in a natural pitch, it will be helpful to do all of the exercises. They will heighten your control and awareness of pitch differences, knowledge you will need for the material on loudness, quality, and intonation in other chapters.

Secondly, I will provide some exercises that will develop a firm grasp on your appropriate pitch and move it into your everyday speaking situations. Finally, you will learn an instant recovery method to help you regain your natural pitch should you lose it in an emotional crisis or other stressful circumstance.

To determine your natural pitch, take a deep breath exactly as you do when yawning and say aloud, "Ahhh . . . I know that." Do it again, making the "ahhh" the most pathetic tone you can manage. Now do it once more and listen closely. The sound the "that" ends on ("Ahhh . . . I know that") will be your natural pitch.

Try it a few more times to get the feel of it. You will hear that the first part of the "ahhh" is on a high pitch level, which drops into your natural pitch at the end of the "ahhh" and is then carried over into the words "I

50

know that."

A variation of this exercise is to say "uh-huh" several times and drag out the "huh" part. The "huh" will come out right on target. Say it again and add the name of someone you know. Here, too, the pitch carries over from the "huh."

Finally, say the word "myth" several times. Now shorten this word by eliminating the "th" at the end. Rapidly repeat "mi mi mi" several times (not the "me me me" the singer uses). Again say "mi mi mi" and add "Milton misses his milk" on the same pitch. Now try "mi mi mi. Mitzie is miffed if a myth is mimicked." In this procedure, the high frontal position for the "m" moved into a lower but still forward placement for the short "i" and created a beautiful natural pitch production. I find this method works especially well with low, gruff voices and for doctors, dentists, and professors who think a dull, low voice creates an objective, intellectual image. In fact, three members of these professions who occasionally telephone me regarding patients teasingly begin their conversations with a "mi mi mi" to reassure me that they are trying to upgrade the voice profile of their impressive professions.

If you are still not satisfied that you have found your best pitch, you can locate it precisely with the Easy One-fourth Method. It requires access to a piano for about five minutes, and many of my students have accomplished this assignment at a piano store. The natural pitch where you will sound the best is generally located about one-fourth of the way up from the bottom of your complete range. In order to find its location, make the lowest sound you can (a grunt will do) and match that note on the piano as nearly as

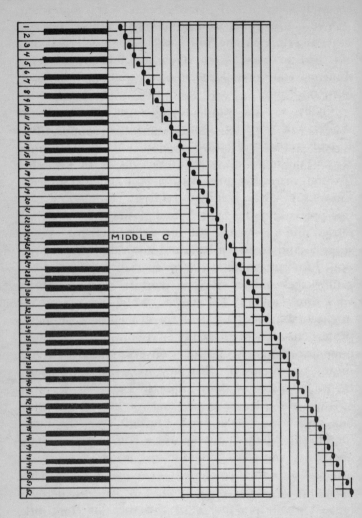

Your natural pitch, where you will sound the best, is generally located about one fourth of the way up from the bottom of your complete range.

possible with one of the white keys. Try somewhere between the tenth and eighteenth keys from the left.

When you find your lowest note, call this key number 1. Then make the highest sound you can, perhaps just a squeak. For males, it will be in falsetto. Match that sound with one of the higher white keys (above key twenty-four) on the piano. Count the number of white keys in between the two sounds. (This could range from between sixteen to twenty-six; men will usually have fewer numbers.) Divide that number by four. Count up the resulting number from your number 1 white key. The key you stop at is your natural pitch.

Now try saying "oh, oh, oh" as you strike the key. If the note seems too high or too low, that's a sure sign you haven't been using that pitch habitually.

Once you discover your natural pitch and realize it's quite different than the one you've been using, you will have found the key to a whole new voice personality.

Now that you've found your natural pitch, the next step is learning how to use it. Knowing where it is and having the ability to use it constantly are two different skills. You have probably already found it difficult to maintain your natural pitch in a sustained conversation.

The following simple exercises will help train your voice to stay on pitch. They are not progressive; you can work through them in any order. The exercises need not interfere with your normal activities, and you may wish to practice while getting ready for work, lingering over morning coffee, or while doing simple routine tasks.

While practicing, you can speak into some sort of a cardboard tube. The tube serves as a response conditioner by capturing the sound and making it seem louder, thereby creating an awareness of what your speaking voice sounds like. After a few practice sessions, you will automatically feel ready to go to work on your new voice the minute you pick up the tube.

1. Find your natural pitch with the yawn-sigh method. Give a good long sigh and then hang onto it as you say the sentences below. Don't read them. Take a quick glance, look up, say "ahhh," then say each sentence out loud.

My name is _____ . I live at _____ . I work at _____ . In my work I _____ . My phone number is _____ . The people in my family are _____ (names of family members). My parents lived most of their lives in _____ . I grew up in _____ . I went to school at _____ .

Once that group of sentences has become natural to you, add these:

In school I was good at _____ . My favorite pastime is _____ . My favorite color is _____ . I am _____ feet and _____ inches tall. I like the _____ (car) best. I like to wear _____ type of clothing. If I could travel I would go to _____ because _____ .

Simply repeat these over and over in your natural pitch voice for about fifteen minutes each daily session. You will find that you can repeat these sentences quite easily in your natural pitch without slipping back.

2. In a week you will have become used to hearing your voice go through the practice exercises at its normal pitch. The next step is to learn how to use that voice in a conversational way.

Continue with the first group of sentences, but add this new group. (Make sure you re-find the right pitch at the beginning of each fifteen-minute session using either the yawn-sigh or the piano method.)

If you are using the yawn-sigh method, take a deep breath and say "ahh" before you say each phrase.

That's the way it is . . . you ought to ask . . . do you want me to . . . how about you . . . how's everything . . . well . . . so what . . . I'm tired . . . take it easy . . . I can't believe it . . . how are you . . . see anybody around . . . what do you mean . . . did you see . . . as far as I can tell . . . just one of those things . . . in a minute . . . give me a little time . . . see you again . . . in about one hour . . . was glad to see you . . . let's go over to . . . if you don't mind . . . not if I can help it . . . aren't you coming . . . believe me . . . I know . . . to put it mildly . . . what's new . . . it's hot today . . . wait for me . . . has the mail come . . . looks like rain . . . you know . . . thank you . . . did I tell you . . . do you know him . . . well now.

During the third week, repeat the last group of phrases with your hands tightly over your ears. You begin to hear and feel the pitch from within your body and become aware of the areas of your mouth and throat that are used to produce the sound. When you progress to step 3, it will help reinforce this awareness, which is essential to making your new pitch a natural part of you.

3. Starting the fourth week, find the highest note you can make and say a few words. You'll sound like a talking chipmunk, but it's important to learn what this high chattering sound feels like. Now try these sentences using these high notes.

My name is _____ . I live at _____ . I work at _____ . In my work I _____ . My phone number is _____ . The people in my family are _____ . My parents lived most of their lives in _____ . I grew up in _____ . I went to school at _____ . I was great at _____ . My favorite color is _____ . My favorite pastime is _____ . I like to eat_____ . If I had a thousand dollars I would buy _____ .

You will feel tension in your neck and face, and the sound will seem to come from high in your head. Cover your ears and repeat the high, squeaky sound. Remove your hands, listen, then cover your ears again as you continue your chipmunk routine. Close your eyes and concentrate on identifying each place you feel the tension of this voice. If you feel that it comes from five or more places, you're really getting tuned in to muscle-feel. Then change to your lowest voice. Put your chin down and in a deep voice repeat the little phrases you just did. Cover your ears with your hands, close your eyes again, and really concentrate on where you feel that sound. You will feel sensation in your chest and vibrations in the bones behind your ears.

Poke around in both a high and low voice until you

feel you know exactly where all the sounds are coming from. Strange as it seems, this is very important preparation for moving comfortably to your natural pitch. Once you know how the muscles feel at both the high and low ends of the range, you will begin to feel uncomfortable whenever you start to move out of your natural voice areas.

4. Find your natural pitch, say a few words, and then begin to chant these sentences.

Guns and drums, drums and guns, guns and drums, drums and guns . . . peas, porridge hot, peas, porridge cold, peas, porridge in the pot, nine days old . . . Joe dropped the jug on his great big toe . . . ho, ho, ho and a bottle of rum . . . I've got plenty of nothing.

After you've mastered these, try some longer phrases. Repeat each sentence at least five times, prolonging each word and keeping it on a single note.

I'll eat soup and salad Monday, Tuesday, Wednesday, Thursday, and Friday. Will you come home in January, February, March, or April?

Cover your ears and repeat this exercise feeling the natural pitch as you did with the higher and lower ranges. Once again, try to decide which muscles are being used to achieve this range.

Now you know what your natural and unnatural pitches feel like. You have learned to put your voice into a natural, sustained pitch area in conversation, and you are beginning to create and build a whole new sound for your voice.

All that's left is to make sure this new pitch not only becomes habitual, but stays with you all the time.

Even at this point, you may find yourself slipping back into old voice patterns now and then in tense situations. Psychologists say, however, that if you can do a task (almost perfectly) for seven days, you'll have developed a habit that will serve you for the rest of your life. Here is one method to make your new pitch a permanent habit.

Trim a standard, lined file card to two inches by three inches. Then draw lines perpendicular to the lines on the card so that you have at least fifteen squares. Whenever you lose your natural pitch, take out your card and blacken a square. You can also say, "I'm coloring the square because I'm aware," as further reinforcement. Naturally, this method requires constant vigilance in order to work, which is precisely what is necessary to ensure that you stay on target. Over a period of several weeks, you will find yourself blackening fewer squares.

In order not to get discouraged, it is important to realize that from time to time, when under pressure, many people revert to their old false pitch. To guard against not recognizing this relapse and neglecting to return to your natural pitch, it is wise to use the buddy system. Take someone into your confidence, tell them what you are trying to do, and ask for their help. Most people are quite flattered that you value their judgement enough to ask for such a favor. Simply arrange some signal between you so that the minute your voice becomes unpleasant, your buddy will let you know.

Alice, a former student of mine, arranged to have Jean, a co-worker, run her finger over her own throat whenever Alice's voice began to climb to its former distressing shrillness. Other signals my students have used effectively have been tapping a pencil, turning off a light, dropping a book, and taking an obvious stretch. If these don't appeal to you, simply work out some of your own. You will only need a small, discreet signal to awaken your consciousness to your temporary relapse.

During emotional experiences, when the going gets rough, you will need another technique. If you suddenly realize in the middle of an intense discussion that you're out of control and you can't seem to regain your natural pitch, try the Instant Bathroom Recovery Method.

You don't really need a bathroom. I chose that name because the method requires instant privacy. A spare office, a storeroom, or even a closet will do. Once you've found it, tilt your head far backward and take a deep breath. Release the breath, lower your head and trunk, and make a long "sssss" sound, as though you were a tire going flat. Keep the air flowing out until you come to the end of your breath. Repeat this process at least four times. At the end of this procedure, try your voice. Chances are that you'll once again be speaking in your correct pitch, for what you have just done is relaxed completely and released the tension you had built up in your voice and body.

The crucial point is that you remember to listen to your voice intermittently to keep them from regaining a hold. You now have techniques to find and maintain your natural pitch, and even an emergency measure for crisis situations. With these tools at your command, you are ready for the next step in attaining full voice power — developing resonance.

FOUR

Righting Your Resonance

Resonance is probably the aspect of voice most poorly understood by the average person. And since the average person knows so little about it, he or she rarely improves his or her resonance throughout an entire lifetime. It may actually dwindle and fade away with age or suddenly change through an injury without anyone ever mentioning the word.

Resonance is not all that elusive once its basic purpose is understood. In fact, it may, for some, be the basic tool for improving their voices. In singing, it differentiates the trained singer from the amateur, and in speaking, it distinguishes the great leaders, actors, and teachers from the "also rans." Resonance is the richness, fullness, deepness, vibrancy that carries the voice to the far corners of the room so that all may hear and feel the meaning that pervades the speaker's message.

Technically resonance is the way the voice is amplified by various structures so that it can be heard. The sounds made in the vocal folds when you speak are almost inaudible, but as they pass through the throat and mouth they are strengthened and beautified (or mangled and distorted). Some of the body structures act as sounding boards and vibrate to increase the sound just like a drum. Others are tube resonators like horns. The mouth cavity is called a cul-de-sac resonator because of the large opening on one side of the resonating area. Using this same principle, the old-fashioned jug bands created a variety of sound by blowing air across crock jugs containing different amounts of liquor. Your voice, then, is the net result of your breath vibrating through the natural instruments of your body, developing loudness, intensity, and that special identifying quality that comes from the size, shape, and mass of your structures.

Each individual learns to focus resonance in a particular part of the body instrument. Some voices sound hollow, others muffled, and still others muffled, and still others irritatingly nasal. Some are denasal, completely lacking nasal quality. The denasal voice sounds deadened and muffled as if the owner had a perpetual cold. If you're around a denasal speaker, you'll find yourself swallowing and clearing your throat and wishing you could get out of range of the germ-spreading menace when in fact a cold may not be involved at all. The irritating voice is produced by an obstruction in the nose, adenoids, postnasal drip, or a bad voice habit. All of these problems can be remedied through changing the old focus to one making better use of your resonators. Sometimes this may prevent the loss of a promotion or even a job. For example, nasality was the tragic cause for trauma for a client of mine who had worked for fifteen years as an executive secretary for one man in a small company. Suddenly, her beloved boss died and his son replaced him. One week later, she was fired on the pretext that the new management wanted to change its whole approach and new personnel would make it easier. To close friends, however, the new executive confided, "Her voice drove me right up the wall!"

This woman had a nasal tone, which is always high pitched and usually on the tense, monotonous side. "Can I change my voice at fifty-five?" the woman anxiously asked. "I feel like the rug has been pulled out from under my feet. I haven't looked for a job for fifteen years. I've been a 'one-company' woman for so long I doubt that I can find another job. Probably he's told everyone he hates my voice."

And he had. But her problem was not irrevocable. She began training and learned a new resonance, and eventually she landed an even better job. It wasn't quick for her, but it was simple. The only difficult part was exerting the self-discipline to practice what must have seemed like dumb exercises, especially since she had a long-standing problem of nasality dating from many childhood tonsil problems.

Tonsillitis does not necessarily have to affect nasality. If the condition wasn't long-standing, was promptly cared for and controlled by medicine, or if the tonsils have been removed, and sufficient tissue is left to adequately close off resonance from the nose, nasality problems will probably not occur. But if you had tonsil problems like the secretary, at a time before antibiotics and when medical supervision was not readily available, it may have provided the exact situation to start you on a lifetime of nasal speech.

During the production of normal resonance, sound passes up the throat through the mouth, bypassing the nose. This requires muscle control of the back of the tongue, which must move up to meet a descending muscle, called the velum or soft palate, located on the roof of the mouth. This action shuts off the sound's resonating in the nasal cavity. The tonsils are located on the sides of the cavity at the back of the mouth. Swollen tonsillar tissue doesn't move easily or well. The infected area is more or less paralyzed and cannot close off the nose with its usual movement. During that time, the child becomes used to not moving these muscles. After the tonsils are removed, the muscles are still sore and may not move well, and so the pattern of least effort often continues.

Common muscle patterns become automatic after many repetitions. The muscle that comes down in the back of the throat to shut off nasality can just as easily slide into the habit of barely moving, especially when its movement was once restricted or infected. Fortunately, you can learn how to walk normally again after a sprained ankle, and if nasality is your problem you can also exercise, strengthen, and learn to use again the muscle that controls nasal resonance.

To determine if you're a nasal speaker, take a tight hold of your nose bridge and loudly say these words: "going, coming, having, doing, talking, walking, eating, finding, keeping, running, sleeping." You will feel the sound vibrating the nose bone at the end of each word. However, if you felt a strong vibration the moment you started the word, you probably are a nasal speaker. None of the sounds that begin those words are nasalized. When correctly pronounced, vowels in the English language are not nasalized, but nasal speakers usually nasalize them all. The "ng" sound at the end of each word is one of the three consonants in the English language that is correctly made with nasal resonance.

To determine if your problem is denasality, hold your nose bridge again and repeat the same words. If you don't feel a nose vibration on the "ing," denasality is the problem. All of the following general exercises to improve resonance will help stop the frustrating sound of denasal resonance as well as the distractingly nasal kinds. For further practice to correct denasality, turn to the lists of words with the "ng" sound in chapter 9 and practice repeating them while holding your nose bridge to be sure you nasalize the "ng" syllable. Make a list of verbs ending in "ing," practice repeating them alone, and then put them into a simple sentence. Practice repeating the sentence holding the end of your nose closed and then again with your nose open. Listen to the difference in sound. You'll be pleased with the difference and will be able to use the materials in the following chapters to better advantage.

The tongue is the primary director of resonance. It has many ways of dividing the mouth cavity and causing the sounds to take on many different qualities. To more readily understand how this happens, try this next exercise.

Put your index finger in your mouth and push down your tongue as you say "ahhh." Now release it. Start another "ahhh" and push your tongue down a little further back. Hear the difference in the sound? The

65

resonance was moved back. Maybe you will want to move your resonance back to give it a fuller, firmer quality.

Your finger is the handiest tool for practicing, but if you're still hesitant from the days when your parents said, "Keep your fingers out of your mouth!" and really feel embarrassed about it, try using a tongue depressor or covering your finger with plastic wrap. If you have some bandage gauze, find it now for this next exercise. Two small pieces torn from a brown paper bag are a workable substitute.

Stick out your tongue and take hold of the tip, using the gauze or the brown paper to keep it from slipping away. Now say "eeee" and then "ahhh." Repeat a couple of times. Release your tongue, repeat "eeee" and "ahhh." Notice the difference in sound. You directed the resonance toward the back of your mouth when you held the tongue out. You will be able to *feel* the difference, too.

The *feeling* of resonance is important. Lots of times it means the difference between experiencing power in your speech and monotony. To gain more of the feel of control of your resonance, make a ditch down the center of your tongue and stick it out of your mouth. You might need a mirror to help you. Actually roll up the sides of your tongue so that a groove appears in the center. Say "ahhh" and "eeee" several times. You will again feel the difference in resonance. With your tongue directing the resonance, it is easy to change the sound by changing the position of the tongue.

The "eeee" sound has the highest tongue position of all the vowels and becomes nasalized the easiest. Nasal speakers will want to work on the "eeee-ahhh" to move the "eeee" sound down a bit to prevent its taking on too much nasality.

It takes a little time to get the feel of redirecting the air coming across your tongue. The next exercise can help. Put your little finger under one side of your tongue. (Right side for right-handed people, left side for left-handed people.) Now as you hold the finger in place, whisper "eee-eye, hey-hi." Be sure you are whispering. You should be making no sound with your vocal folds. To be sure, put the fingers of your other hand on your Adam's apple as you say "eee-eye, hey-hi." If you feel a vibration, you aren't whispering.

Many people still make sounds when they whisper. If you're a noisy whisperer, take time to learn the quiet kind through this exercise. Should you ever lose your voice, you will need the quiet whisper to recover. The noisy one will even make your laryngitis worse. Learn to whisper so that the only sound you hear is the shaping of the air by your tongue and its surroundings. Not only will you feel what your speech air is doing, but you'll also develop awareness of the movements of lips, jaw, and tongue. Try to concentrate on their shape and movement as you do this next exercise to develop resonance.

You have grooved your tongue outside your mouth. Now groove it inside. Unless you're very well-coordinated, you'll probably need to use your lips to help. Do the "eeee-ahhh" combination several times as loudly and clearly as you can muster. (If someone answers you, you'll know you were loud enough.) You will feel the resonance in two different areas in the back of your mouth. Now see if you can feel the resonance in two additional spots as you keep your tongue grooved and say "eeee-ahhh, eye, oh." Tongue grooving puts you in tune with its tenseness. You may even be getting a "tongue ache." So at this point, you will learn to relax your tongue.

Groove your tongue and make the "eeee" sound, then let it uncurl as you whisper "ahhh." Groove it, say "eye," relax it, whisper "ohhh." Listen carefully as you make the grooved tongue "eye" sound again, then ungroove and say loudly "ahhh." If you hear the differences in resonance, your ears have become trained as resonance monitors. Of course, it began the moment you began the resonance training. One of the best qualifications the ears have is that they never stop hearing. They don't always listen, but they do hear, and changes in the way you do things happen whether you listen or not.

If you made the two five-by-seven-inch pieces of cardboard for checking how you sound in the first chapter, get them out now for the next few exercises. If you didn't, make them now. If you're really unable, unwilling, or uninterested in making your cardboard ear helpers, you can use a less efficient substitute, your hands. Cup them around your ears to hear a louder version of how you think you sound to others. Put them tightly in front of your ears, your thumbs pushing into your cheeks and your fingers pointing straight up, to experience approximately what others hear. Try reading these famous sayings, using either your cardboards or your hands. Remember, in front of your ear is what they hear, behind your ear is what you hear.

1. Time is the most valuable thing a man has to spend.

2. The supreme happiness of life is the conviction we are loved.

3. My life is in the hands of any fool who makes me lose my temper.

4. Habit is the best of servants or the worst of masters.

5. We give advice by the bucket, but take it by the grain.

6. People are lonely because they build walls instead of bridges.

7. Most people are in favor of progress; it's the changes they dislike.

Don't think too much about the content as you listen. Thinking about content will interfere with listening to the changes you have already begun making in your resonance. And now you are going to make further changes.

To begin, grit your teeth. Then let your mouth hang open. Grit your teeth again and then relax. Open your jaw wide and say "ahhh." Close it lightly and say "ahhh" again. You will notice the difference in tone. When your jaw is open, more sound comes out and usually the quality is better.

Even though you'll never use your jaws in speech as much as you will use them in these exercises, you will need to learn to chew as lavishly as possible. To help feel your jaw working, place your finger just below your earlobe and feel your jaw move as you do some wide chewing. You may have to feel around as you chew to find the best spot to check your jaw movement. Now say, "I am going out," and make your jaws come open as wide as possible. Open them very widely on

"I," "am," "ing," and "out." You will notice that your jaw movement moved your resonance. Listen carefully as you say, "I like apples and apricots." The wider your jaws the better. Since many of us have jaws that are a bit out of place, you may hear some popping and cracking and even a noise in your ears. But don't worry. On the whole, jaws are the sturdiest part of the body. They are the parts of most animals that remain after everything else has decomposed. Anthropologists, dentists, and many other specialists are beginning to look at the jaw with new respect.

Dr. Harold Gelb, professor at the College of Medicine and Dentistry of New Jersey, says that the jaw is the center of balance for the human body. His book, *Temporal Mandibular Joint Dysfunction*, describes treatment for jaws that are out of balance, causing discomfort in the neck, head, back, and so on.

Early cave people could have first discovered how to vary sounds by simply moving their jaws, and later settled on certain movements and sounds for specific meanings. The first speech may have originated between cavemen disputing the ownership of a fresh carcass. One growl expressed, "That's mine, and I intend to eat every bit of it." Softer, prolonged sounds conveyed, "We've been buddies for a long time. I'm hungry. Please share a little piece with me." Increased jaw movement with intense, loud, explosive resonance could have eloquently settled the discussion by implying that a skull would be crushed if any attempt to take was initiated.

Working from this orientation, Dr. Emil Froeschels developed the "chewing approach" for individuals with fluency problems as well as a great number of other problems associated with voice. Although both therapists and clients dislike this seemingly unsophisticated approach, the consistent reports of its efficiency convinced me to incorporate it into my practice. Even extremely snobbish clients are impressed by the Viennese Dr. Froeschels's accomplishments and his article "Chewing Method as Therapy," which appeared in the *Archives of Otalaryngology*, LVI. When they realize that this simple method can give them a lifetime technique for reestablishing resonance when they've slipped away from it, as well as a painless approach to its development, they eagerly pocket my printed card with these abbreviated instructions.

Chewing Therapy — use a small mirror for all practice.

1. Inhale deeply. Say "ha" until out of breath.
2. Inhale deeply, say "ha," and then start slow, exaggerated chewing of "ha" until out of air.
3. Inhale deeply, say "ha," chew it, incorporate lively, expansive tongue motion in each "ha." Repeat ten times.
4. Check for nasality. Fingers hold bridge of nose, inhale, chew "ha," increase tongue and jaw movement to limit.
5. Vibration in nose bridge during four indicates need for more tongue and jaw movement until no nasal vibration is felt.
6. Inhale deeply. Start chewing "ha one, ha two, ha three . . ." until out of air. Air, sound, movement, and words must continuously blend. *Keep the sound coming!*
7. Inhale deeply. Start chewing "ha." Add days of

the week, months, names of all fruits and vegetables you know. Air, sound, gross tongue, and
jaw motion synchronized, or repeat step 6.
8. Exaggerated chewing, continuous sound as any
newspaper or magazine is read aloud. Concentrate on feel of tongue motion.
9. Refer carefully to mirror to reduce jaw movements to one-half of those used for steps 2
through 8, continue reading aloud using slower,
precise tongue motion.
10. Telephone a friend about routine matter, monitor jaw and lip movement with mirror, reduce
chewing to minimum to maintain mellow resonance with precise diction.

I have heard harshness, nasality, and unpleasant
pitches disappear during chewing practice, but often
more help is needed to use the newly discovered
resonance in daily speech. The focus on taking deep
breaths during the chewing practices cannot be emphasized enough. Now techniques to help you control your breath to manipulate resonance will be
explored.

The first exercise will help you feel what the push
of air does for consonant sounds. Put your fists on
your breastbone and give a brisk push inward each
time you slowly say "puh, buh, tuh, duh, kuh, guh."
You will feel the air push the back of your throat. Try
"ruh, muh, luh, suh, nuh." Your pitch, as well as
resonance, should also be in the right range. This
particular exercise helps breathing, pitch, and resonance by using the muscles involved in each. Getting
the feel of these muscles in action aids you in being

able to consciously control them.

The following exercise promotes even greater control. Yawn—open your jaws as wide as you can. Yawn again and make a loud "ahhh" as you let the air out, while simultaneously tapping your chest with the tips of your fingers. Listen for a wavering tone as you tap. You have just added vibrato to your resonance. See if you can do it again without tapping your chest. Of course if you've had training in vocal music, that will be old stuff to you. Some people can create the feel of vibrato by making a tone and then quickly shaking their head. Learning to feel vibrato and produce it gives you added control over your resonance. Obviously you won't use vibrato in your daily speech, but it is good to practice it often to increase your control of resonance.

You can shake the sound around in many other ways, too. The belt vibrators that you find in gyms or can buy through most of the large catalog stores produce strong vibrato. I use one with all of my speech clients. It cures self-consciousness quickly as well as encouraging experimentation with voice. The belt vibrator can help you stabilize your newly acquired natural pitch. Go up and down the scale, or simply hang on to any note and see what happens to it as you shake.

Flexibility in any muscle goes a long way toward developing the coordination that supports an easy, natural sounding voice. Strength helps too. Put all of your fingers on your stomach and give a sharp push each time you say "ho." Try to do it twenty times. Do ten more and make your stomach move as sharply without using your fingers to push. This time try to visualize the air jumping up from your stomach and out your mouth. That's really feeling the power of resonance. Many speech teachers still call this "projecting the voice." Actually, it's just learning to purposefully use resonance.

The next resonance muscle you will concentrate on is the soft palate. Use a mirror for this exercise. It always helps to see as well as feel what you're doing. Open your mouth wide and say these sounds: "nnn, ga, nnn, ga, nnn, ka, nnn, ka." Watch the back part of your tongue rise to meet the soft palate muscle. The soft palate, or velum, moves down. As I said before, it's the muscle that closes off the nasal resonance. It is also the muscle that singers work hard to learn to raise high for a fuller sound. If you can, swallow with your mouth open and you'll see how the velum comes down for swallowing. Did you know you swallow more than 2000 times a day? Of course it's impossible to count, because most of the time you are swallowing saliva and the muscles move so slightly that you're not aware of it. But the velum is the slowest moving muscle in the body, and for some people, it's the laziest. If you're really nasal and don't want to be, this is the muscle that has to be strengthened. Improving velar muscle tone can help alleviate another common nose problem — snoring! Recent research has shown that velar laxness causes snoring and that this increases as age advances. All of the procedures for the control of the velum will help head off problems associated with the velum.

I have discovered that the use of one commercial instrument can speed the process of velar control. A Water-Pik can help stimulate the velum to more activity. In fact, some children who drooled over-came it after consistent use of the Water-Pik. Part of the reason is that the pik encouraged the children to swallow rapidly. Quick swallowing combined with the stimulation of the jet of water built up the draggy muscle. If nasality is your biggest resonance problem, you might find the investment worthwhile and enjoy the fringe benefits of your teeth surviving longer because of healthier gums.

In order to check your progress as to whether you have learned to shut off your nasal resonance with your soft velum, squeeze your nose bridge and say, "mmm, ahhh." If you still feel a vibration in your nose bridge when you say "ahhh," you have some more work to do. The next exercise will help, and even if you didn't feel the vibration do the exercise anyway—it will sharpen your awareness of front and back resonance. To clean up the ah, that is, take out the nasality, do this series of sounds: "mmm, bah, ah, mmm, buh, ohh, mmm, buh, ooo (as in who), mmm, buh, aaa (as in cat)." By moving the sound from the back to the front of the mouth, and then back again on the "ahhh," you should begin to feel and hear the difference in front and back resonance. Here's a few more that work the same way: "nnn, duh, ohh, nnn, duh, ahh, nnn, duh, eee, nnn, duh, aaa (as in hay), nnn, duh, ooo (as in who)." Now that you've caught on, you can do more combinations that switch from nasal to non-nasal, and from the back of the mouth to the front. (For example, "ing, tuh," and any vowel; "mmm, luh" and any vowel; "nnn, puh," and any vowel.) It takes real devotion to do that kind of practice, but it pays off in awareness of what's going on in the back of your mouth for resonance. When you feel you've mastered these simple sounds, you can progress to the following words and sentences.

Take a deep breath and say the word "song" three times, getting louder each time. Listen for the lingering nasal resonance on the end. Try the same with "long" and then "dong." Be sure to get louder each time and hold on to the word until you run out of breath. Nasal resonance can have a mellow ring, as you've just experienced. For contrast to the nasal ring, try the next phrase. Take a deep breath and say, "Life and living is all I have." Remember to open your jaws widely. If you did it correctly, you should have felt the stomach muscles moving, too. Here are more famous lines to practice your new resonance: "Alone, alone, all, all alone," and "Surrounded, surrounded, always surrounded!"

To help you begin to use more resonance in your speaking, turn back to the little words and phrases in the previous chapter and practice them while trying to keep your tongue tip pointed up. As the resonance director, your tongue tip can easily be your best watchdog for good resonance. Practicing with a hand mirror will help you gain a stronger image of how this feels and will help you to remember to open your mouth. For a super strong sound, do the exercise in an enclosed shower and experience the ultimate in resonance power.

Through all of these exercises you have progressed to understanding the value of resonance in speaking. It is a way to increase the intensity of your voice without increasing your effort. In fact, effort is actually decreased because the best tones are produced by relaxing the resonating cavities and keeping them as open as possible. All singers learn to vary resonators instead of increasing intensity or loudness, and this skill is equally important to anyone who wants an interesting variety in his or her voice during everyday conversation or wants protection against bouts of hoarseness.

A final check to determine if you have learned to manipulate your resonators is to speak into the microphone of a recorder while watching the intensity needle. Back away from the recorder as you continue speaking and increase your intensity by varying your resonators rather than expending more energy so that the needle registers no difference from when you were close. This can be achieved, as you have learned, by increasing intensity with your jaws, tongue, and breath as well as appropriate tone placement. If you found you also became louder, don't despair. Loudness is one of the easiest techniques to voice power. Both resonance and variations in loudness will enhance the voice power foundation you have laid by learning to use your breath, finding your natural pitch, and developing control of both. In the next chapter, you will explore the concept of loudness and learn to make it work for you.

FIVE

Lucid Power through Likable Loudness

Loudness is not a welcome word today. It has become associated with noise pollution and unpleasant personalities and is now known to be able to cause illness, injury, and even death. Modern people are inundated with noise. A news report recently stated that noises in the kitchen reached levels eighty decibels and above. Schools located near airports report lower achievement for their students because of the ever-present noise. Even plants are reported to wither with constant noise exposure. Loudness is regarded as undesirable because it has become associated with noise. We need to differentiate between loudness in voice and loudness in noise. You are in no way headed toward becoming "a loud person" by working on loudness level. Instead, you may actually be headed toward being considered an interesting person for the first time in your life. How many people do you know who are part of the silent throng? You often barely know what they are saying. You don't remember who they are. They're just people who work in the same place you do, ride the same buses, and talk on the same monotonous level that you are also might use.

People may think they are choosing to talk loudly or

softly in a situation, but loudness is really a habit that is reinforced by the situation in which they spend the most time. Teachers who speak loudly in the morning are not likely to become quiet as the day progresses, neither do the soft-spoken physician's tones become more distinct toward the end of the day. People in many professions have chronic loudness problems that prevent them from achieving success. A voice that is too soft may not receive much attention, and a voice that is too loud may arouse resistance, if not hostility. In addition, chronically loud talkers who have not been trained to breathe correctly, to maintain natural pitch, and to speak at an appropriate rate with good resonance may have frequent laryngitis, nodules, ulcerated vocal folds, or other symptoms of abuse. Both chronically loud speakers and those who are not loud but maintain constant intensity have tense vocal mechanisms, not to mention bodies. Learning to vary their loudness will help them avoid voice tension problems even if the other aspects of voice power have not been learned.

The loudness or softness of a person's speech level is connected intimately with self-image. If you chronically speak much too loudly or softly, first consider your self-image.

For example, in my clinical experience, a too-soft voice signals low self-esteem and is a cry for help. Many very soft speakers are extremely critical of themselves and others. They attract losers to themselves, continuing the cycle of being let down about themselves and others. Many seek my help because they think that if they learn to express themselves better, talk louder, speak plainer, or overcome their fear of speaking before groups they can achieve their goals. Loudness can also be a symptom of a low self-image. The loudness compensates for the lack of success experienced in some part of life. Ferocious-sounding husbands who habitually yell at their wives and constantly shout orders to their children may not be receiving recognition at work. It is true that skills can raise a self-image, but many times the old self-image sabotages their efforts.

Self-image limits our ability to achieve goals. Like an air conditioner thermostat, it clicks on at a certain limit and blasts cold air on our aspirations. A low self-image replays memories of failure, poverty, guilt, sickness, anger, fear, or loneliness, so deep in the subconscious that the person does not even picture the original situation causing the emotion but rather feels a vague uneasiness. Success invokes discomfort rather than joy. When the limit of a person's expectations is passed—something has been won, inherited, bought, or found—the need to apologize is felt. Soon the rut of underachievement is back. Often the process is accompanied by a "streak of bad luck"; a cut finger, minor car accident, loss, annoyance with a friend, with more swearing than usual throughout it all. The whole experience becomes one more confirmation of a negative self-image.

Fortunately, you can work to improve your self-image and become the person that you want to be. You can turn your energies toward creating this improved self-image. There are many changes you can achieve yourself using your thoughts and voice. It does not help to just deny negative attitudes and habits, as denial often reinforces behavior. When you hear yourself repeating a bad habit, simply say firmly, "That's an error. I actually am smart, effective, efficient," or another corrective adjective. Getting acquainted with your limiting thoughts and deciding on their replacements are parts of the voice power process of setting goals. Read over this list of statements from high achievers who have developed strong self-images. Decide which ones could help you achieve your potential and your full voice power. Which ones are part of your long-range goals?

1. I am taking the steps to put my personal life in order. (Positive self-discipline)
2. I can stay with a task until it is completed. (Positive self-control)
3. I have listed my life goals, my short term goals, and my "right now" tasks and am doing the requirements of each. (Positive self-direction)
4. I adjust quickly to changes in people, situations, and places without depression, anxiety, fear, or grief. (Positive self-control)
5. I anticipate success in all my undertakings every day. (Positive self-expectancy)
6. I include a new interest, recreation, hobby, sport, craft, etc. in my life each year to continually expand the use of my brain. (Positive self-enhancement)
7. I have a deep sense of well-being that is unshaken by news reports, failures, or death. (Positive self-expectancy)
8. I use my mind as a tool to purposefully direct its conscious functioning as well as its unconscious functioning. (Positive self-discipline)

9. I maintain a clean, well-groomed appearance, I have no habits destructive to my health (smoking, excessive eating, drinking, fast driving, excessive habitual physical and mental exertion). (Positive self-esteem)

10. I am honest with myself about my beliefs, the roles I am playing, and what I expect to gain from them. (Positive self-awareness)

11. I take full responsibility for communicating clearly and simply information I am assigned to dispense. (Positive self-projection)

12. I understand that the job or role I am now fullfilling is required for my personal growth and therefore do it as well as possible. (Positive self-awareness)

13. I discard unbecoming clothing, avoid styles not suited to my bodily structure or comfort, and reflect through my clothing an orderly, attractive image. (Positive self-projection)

14. I take full responsibility for scheduling my time so that I do not rush or pressure others into hurrying. (Positive self-dimension.)

15. I have a deep conviction of personal worth and do not give in to feelings that I do not meet standards or am unlovable. (Positive self-esteem)

16. I continually inwardly compliment myself for each task successfully completed. I praise others continuously for good performance, thoughtfulness, attractiveness, etc. (Positive self-motivation)

17. I realize that stinginess with money or possessions are attitudes that impede me from increasing my supply and hinder my positive

relationships with others. (Positive self-dimension)

18. I've eliminated the "have to," "should," and "wish I could" from my vocabulary and use instead "I want to," "I can," "I plan to." (Positive self-motivation)

19. I visualize myself doing needed jobs, accomplishing my dreams, always being in perfect health, and continuously expressing my best nature. (Positive self-enhancement)

20. I set daily priorities related to my goals but always considering the rights, needs, convenience, and fairness to others in carrying them forward. (Positive self-direction)

One of your immediate goals is improving awareness and use of intensity and loudness. Intensity is the energy applied to any force; loudness cannot be increased without increasing it. Technically, loudness is the degree of amplification of a particular sound wave, and intensity is the weight of the sound. Both are created by the interaction of pitch, resonance, and breath support.

Often it is best to increase intensity without increasing loudness at all. For example, many effective figures in the women's movement have a soft but intense firmness that dramatically conveys determination supported by love.

Increasing intensity and loudness will make you a participant in any group. People who have never been asked to contribute are suddenly discovered when they increase their voices' loudness and intensity. People who use too much may at times wish to fade into the background. They, too, can benefit from becoming aware of the source of their energy and learning to control it.

The first step in learning to manage your loudness level is to make sure you are willing to share the emotions that changes in loudness and intensity convey. Can you let others know you feel anger, happiness, sadness, disgust, and other emotions? Many of the exercises teach loudness and intensity variations by marking stress with underlining. This can work wonders. In daily communication, however, it would be laborious to analyze forthcoming conversations and plan the topics and placement for intensity and loudness. Expressing your real emotions is a more natural and practical approach.

The second step in using intensity and loudness effectively is to learn to control intensity. A side benefit will be that you will learn your maximum intensity while you are in control rather than in an emergency. When told to scream, one person could not even squeak. "I think I had such a prohibition built up concerning screaming that I just could not do it even though I opened my mouth and strained all of my neck muscles in the effort."

First experiment with single vowel sounds (many people hesitate to use their most intense intensities with words at first). Take a deep breath and very softly say "ah." Continue making the sound, increasing the force slowly to build up to the strongest possible "ah." Then let the sound diminish gradually until it completely dies away in a whisper. Try this with "oh" and "ooo." Observe whether the increase in intensity was accompanied by a loudness increase or a raise in pitch.

Experiment with these three sounds to develop the ability to increase intensity without climbing to a higher pitch.

After this experiment in controlled intensity, you can establish your three basic levels of loudness. Softly say the phrase "don't do that," as though you didn't want to be overheard in a crowd. Repeat it at a level you might use to admonish someone in the privacy of home or office. Finally, repeat it loud enough to stop an action you can see occurring across the street. Use your top limit. This may be the weapon that saves your life someday.

Experiment with these three levels until you can produce them easily. Try various phrases; "I love you" is a popular phrase that is used on these levels by everyone at some time. "Come here," "where's my key?" and "who did that?" are three close competitors for practice phrases used most frequently by my clients.

Next, go between your top and bottom levels in small steps. You need to know the territory between your maximum and minimum power.

Say the vowel "oh" in a soft voice. Repeat it with slightly increasing intensity. Continue repeating it a little louder each time until you reach your limit. You can probably manage to use fifteen different loudness levels. Start at your loudest level and see how many steps you can use to reach your softest. Be sure you pause between each step. As you get close to the bottom, you'll become breathy. Keep it as clear as you can before you hit a whisper.

To get better acquainted with the effort required to achieve different loudness levels, take three sounds, "l," "r," and "z," and prolong each as long as you can. It's going to be difficult to make any of these sounds loudly. That will give you the chance to feel more precisely exactly what you do to produce loudness. Take a deep breath and make the "l" sound as loudly as you can. Pause and remember your middle level of loudness. Now make the sound at that level. Finally, stop and remember your softest level without whispering and make the sound again. Do the same thing with the "r" and "z" sounds. Each time you complete an exercise, you add to your ability to use levels of loudness with control. To increase your control even more, try this next exercise.

Take the sound "ah" and try to hold it for twenty seconds with a light intensity. The loudness level should be near the bottom of your quiet range. Now repeat it at a moderate intensity and try for twenty-five seconds. You will use more of your muscles to extend your sound the extra five seconds using your middle level of intensity. Now try your strongest intensity. See how many different muscles you can feel working as you take a deep breath. You'll need all the air you can get to keep the "ah" going. This does not mean you will use your loudest voice. You will instead be giving it as much energy as you can. At your loudest level, you would have a problem. You will probably find that you ran out of air more quickly this time. If you were able to extend the "ah" to the full twenty-five seconds in your most intense voice, you really got in touch with what your sound power feels like in your body. At the most intense level, some of my students say they felt the ends of their fingertips and their toes pulsing.

According to the research cited by George Leonard in *The Silent Pulse*, we are all in touch with each other rhythmically through a pulse beat that we aren't even aware of. The moment someone begins speaking, the listener begins subliminal movement in rhythm with what is being said. The actual words being spoken do not have to be intelligible to the listener. The emphatic rhythm comes only from the sound. Leonard points out that it is this basic attunement on a level we don't recognize that causes people to act the way they do. The mobs that followed some of the great villains of history were actually bound together by this pulse. It can reach such a peak that reason doesn't function. People are lynched, tortured, and murdered by mobs acting in rhythmic attunement. Awareness of the intensity of the voice vibration and its potential for good or evil will help you to monitor its effect on you in familiar life situations. The hypnosis ascribed to television, the lure of the racetrack, the attraction of the casino slot machine, all are reinforced through the pulse beat of others as well as the charisma of certain politicians, ministers, leaders of special interest groups, and of course, your closest associates. These intensity exercises will help make you custodian of your intensity and will sharpen your discrimination of the power latent in the intensity of others.

Speak each of these commands with light, moderate, and extreme intensity. Try to say each word with an equal amount of energy. This will initiate an awareness of the way intensity affects meaning. If you find this even intensity difficult, you probably have a programmed meaning associated with a varied intensity for these familiar word groups.

1. Make another choice.
2. Follow the guard.
3. Take the next number.
4. Wait for the next car.
5. Run faster.
6. Do it now.
7. Begin slowly.
8. Smile and say yes.
9. Come with me.
10. Don't wait for me.
11. Play it now.
12. Ring that bell.
13. Stand back.
14. Throw them out.
15. Blow the whistle.
16. Jump the fence.
17. Hand me the money.
18. Make an effort.
19. Look under the table.
20. Show him now.
21. Move it now.
22. Stay to the right.
23. Take smaller bites.
24. Step down carefully.

To keep each word on the same level of intensity is a tricky chore. It actually is easier to vary them. Large variations in intensity is one of the key aspects of the powerful voice. They keep the listeners on their toes. Say the following phrases, pronouncing the italicized word with greater intensity than the others.

1. The bird *has* flown.
2. Night *must* end.
3. *John* knew it.
4. *We* went home.
5. Please call *us*.
6. *I* came back.
7. Show *him* the way.
8. The dog bit *her*.
9. *All* of America.
10. Not since *yesterday*.
11. Late *in* July.
12. I'll be at *home*.
13. Look on the *table*.
14. Hand the man a *book*.
15. *Don't* ask questions.
16. It's *not* the thing to do.
17. *That's* the answer.
18. The clock struck *one*.
19. I will *if* I can.
20. Don't count on *me*.
21. That's *especially* nice.
22. *Who* answered the phone.
23. I want to, *but* I can't.
24. Take the *next* bus.

To help get your voice really tuned in to the shades of intensity that occur in every sentence you speak, try repeating the following short phrases using first two light intensity words followed by two heavy intensity words. Remember every exercise you do moves you closer to bringing intensity changes into your daily conversation. When the effects of these exercises begin to emerge in daily conversation, you'll know your voice power is expanding.

1. *That cold* cold ground.
2. *This is* your last chance.
3. *He grabbed* the last one.
4. *Follow now,* or walk alone.
5. *Choose two* red ones.
6. *They ran* over fast.
7. *Be there,* or else.
8. *Go far* and see more.
9. *Are you* going now?
10. *Write me* once in a while.
11. *Either this* one or that one.
12. *From noon* till midnight.
13. *From here* to eternity.
14. *Buy now,* sell later.
15. *I will,* he won't.
16. *Call us,* not them.

Now reverse the intensity changes and give the italicized words only light intensity. Notice how the meaning changes.

Intensity and loudness are the main tools of the news commentator. Have you ever listened to exactly the same news read by different announcers and had the vague feeling that you were hearing exactly the opposite of what you heard before? Distorting the news according to a particular bias is easily done by varying loudness. Try it yourself with the news report below and change the loudness and intensity on the words underlined.

The United States government wound up the fiscal year'nine billion dollars in the <u>red</u>. One reason for the deficit was a carry-over of <u>bills incurred</u> by the <u>Democratic</u> administration. Others were disappointing tax collections and the inability of the Republicans to achieve all of their promised economics. The administration re--ains *confident* that despite a *tradition* of *expensive* government, the margin of deficit will be *further reduced*.

Now read it again and see how much you can blast the Republicans by changing the words you amplify. The underlined ones will do the trick.

The United States government wound up the fiscal year *nine billion dollars* in the *red*. One reason for the deficit was a carry-over of bills incurred by the Democratic administration. *Others* were disappointing tax collections and the *inability* of the *Republicans* to achieve all of their *promised* economics. The administration remains confident that despite a tradition of expensive government, the margin of *deficit* will be further reduced.

Of course, loudness is usually not the only technique capitalized on to editorialize what was supposed to be nonpartisan wire-service news. Timing and quality as well as pitch create the bias. Of course, if it's televised, the movements of the newscaster can also help slant the meaning. If he knits his brows and leans forward with concern, the message takes on a different flavor than if he stands upright and smiles occasionally as he reads. Of course, we do the same thing with the "news" items we pass along. Read the item below and see if you can slant it in one way to express happiness for the family, then read it so that the husband becomes unlikable.

Our neighbors are finally moving out. He was given

a transfer to a company in Hawaii. I hope he likes his work better there. I understand he left his wife here to sell the house while he went ahead to Honolulu. The house was on the market for six months and then was finally purchased by a woman who liked their cat as much as the house. Of course, he was more than willing to give up the cat to sell the house. They both agreed the cat would be happier.

You now see how the use of loudness variations in a mischievous way can change news into gossip. In fact you probably already know several people who are proficient with their loudness variations in this way. They'll provide lots of good practice situations for you to hear and watch what happens to information accompanied by loudness and intensity changes.

One of my clients could analyze another's loudness variations very quickly and could do the exercises easily, but always slipped right back into a confidential whispering voice in conversation. I borrowed a technique developed to catch people who were pretending to have a hearing loss to avoid the draft or to collect insurance. I played a tape of crowd noise and asked him to continue speaking to me as best he could. Of course, he adjusted quickly and spoke louder and slower. His motivation was increased by competing sounds. Persons with real hearing loss cannot perceive increased volume and so don't compensate. I suggested he practice all of his lessons from then on with the tape. Any competing noise will do as well. You can always find a place on your radio dial that provides free static. Sometimes drowning out a newscaster you don't like may give you the motivation you need to practice.

Some of my students have disliked commercials on television so much that they kept practice materials nearby to drown them out and to see how powerful their voice could be with professional competition that was planned to seduce the eyes and ears of the hardiest resisters.

That kind of practice is good preparation for speaking before an audience. Most of the time a microphone makes up for the size of the room, its acoustics, and audience distance. It would be great if they always worked perfectly or if there were always someone available to fix a squealing mike or one that suddenly goes dead. If you've taken the time to do your voice work so far, you could do a good job of being your own microphone. Here's my technique. First, I shout at the top of my range to ask the audience to be quiet. I tell them that without the microphone, I must cancel my talk unless they cooperate fully. They must sit as still as possible, refrain from shuffling papers or conversing with others around them. I don't begin until I see and feel that cooperation. Then, of course, I speak more slowly with as much resonance as possible, with lots of inflection, facial expressions, and movements, and of course, I increase my overall level of loudness. It takes a lot of air, but I find that comes automatically if I'm paying attention to my rate of speaking and loudness level. Successful political speakers use these techniques all the time, even with microphones. They never begin speaking again until the laughter, applause, and disruptions from audience movement have died down. Remember, unless you are easily heard, you don't have a chance of getting your thoughts to their target.

The right level of loudness presents you as a strong

capable person. It is enhanced by your natural pitch, requires a good breath support from your abdomen, and is resonated easily from a point best for you. Learning how to use timing to increase your voice power will refine the skills you have mastered to vary loudness, and become aware of pitch, and right resonance. The next chapter will not only show you how to use timing, but also develop your overall understanding of the underlying problems of rapid speakers as well as the slow talkers.

SIX

Timing, a Personality Dimension of Voice Power

Speech rate is a matter of split seconds, yet it affects every aspect of a voice. Neither rapid nor excessively slow speech has good resonance. Speech rate can distort articulation; limit pitch changes; and change quality, intonation, and emphasis. The fast speaker shortens sounds, eliminating many possibilities for varying intensity, loudness, and pitch. The slower speaker can distort sounds so greatly that they become unintelligible.

Talking very quickly creates many communications problems. Everyone has had difficulty at some time understanding an impatient waiter or a rushed store clerk. More subtly, we tend to feel uneasy around the fast-talker. The stereotype of the fast talker is a very busy person who cannot be trusted: the smooth lawyer, the slick con artist, the high-pressure salesman. When we feel pushed into believing or buying something, we put up a red flag. Because the fast talker fails to transmit information at an understandable rate, many messes are caused about which he or she then complains. Difficulties with spouses, children, and friends can be caused by this fast communicating.

While the fast talker is generally thought to be very busy, the "lazy, good-for-nothing lout" image often falls on the slow speaker. A person who speaks overly slowly, hesitates often, and responds slowly is thought to be stupid, maybe even retarded. Think of the stereotype of retarded speech portrayed by actors: slow, hesitant speech.

Actually the slow speaker often is a very brilliant, thoughtful person but is overly cautious and concerned about his or her influence on others. He or she may be troubled by a lack of confidence in speaking situations. The slowness to respond and wearisome speech may be the telltale reminder of feelings of unworthiness, fear of punishment for being wrong, or feeling intellectually inadequate to parents and peers that began in childhood. The teenaged years, no doubt, were a disaster. Unfortunately the slow speaker seldom realizes the frustration slow speech arouses in others, and how often he or she may be avoided for that reason.

Communication problems are caused by slow talkers, too. Distorted sounds and the draggy lack of variety can make speech incomprehensible. A client who visited a relative in a small southern town told me that it was several days before she could be sure of the local speech. I asked for a tape of some conversations. Indeed, the omission of sounds, lack of variety, and local vocabulary made the conversations virtually unintelligible.

Unfortunately, as the rate of speech is closely related to personality, it is one of the most difficult aspects of a voice to permanently change. Rapid speech is often associated with a hurry-up mentality. Interrupting, completing others' sentences, glancing at watches, and looking beyond the speaker are other characteristics of the communications problems of the habitual fast talker. They are poor listeners, because they are preoccupied with their next task and their next concern.

There are more reasons than communicating to think about whether you feel constantly pressured and in a hurry: one way the body deals with this demand to rush through activities without time to unwind is the sudden heart attack. Mary Bolton, who conducts cardiovascular nursing workshops across the country, uses a Hurry Sickness Index to help her participants evaluate their own behavior. The questions will definitely influence your willingness to work on the exercises that will follow.

HURRY SICKNESS INDEX

Please indicate how often each of the following applies to you in daily life.

	Always or Usually	Some- times	Seldom or Never
1. Do you find yourself rushing your speech?	____	____	____
2. Do you hurry other peoples' speech by interrupting them with "umhn, umhm" or by completing their sentences for them?	____	____	____

3. Do you hate to wait in line? _____ _____ _____

4. Do you seem to be short of time to get everything done? _____ _____ _____

5. Do you detest wasting time? _____ _____ _____

6. Do you eat too fast? _____ _____ _____

7. Do you drive over the speed limit? _____ _____ _____

8. Do you try to do more than one thing at a time? _____ _____ _____

9. Do you become impatient if others do something too slowly? _____ _____ _____

10. Do you seem to have little time to relax and enjoy the time of day? _____ _____ _____

11. Do you find yourself overcommitted? _____ _____ _____

12. Do you jiggle your knees or tap your fingers? _____ _____ _____

13. Do you think about other things during conversations? _____ _____ _____

14. Do you walk fast? _____ _____ _____

15. Do you hate dawdling after a meal? _____ _____ _____

16. Do you become irritable if kept waiting? _____ _____ _____

17. Do you detest losing in sports or games? _____ _____ _____

18. Do you clinch your fists or tighten your neck or jaw muscles? _____ _____ _____

19. Does your concentration sometimes wander while you think about what's coming up later? _____ _____ _____
20. Are you a competitive person? _____ _____ _____

Although a high-pressured person will not be able to permanently slow down the rate of speech, he or she can learn to repeat information and to vary rate with the complexity of the material. The first step is simply to discover how fast you talk in comparison with others. Speaking rate is generally similar to speed of reading aloud. Time yourself while reading the passage below. If you usually stumble over words, repeat phrases, and have difficulty reading meaningfully, first become familiar with the passage by reading it several times.

Read in your everyday style, without implementing any of the other voice power skills learned so far. If intensity and loudness changes are used, for example, you will read slower than normal. Don't read in a whisper. Since whispered speech does not require complete closing of the vocal folds, you may do it at a much faster speed. Of course, don't purposefully read any slower or faster than you ordinarily would speak, we want your "raw" rate, rather than your voice power rate.

The improvement of memory has been a matter of concern since the Greeks first began to study oratory in the fifth century before Christ. In its earliest beginnings, Greek literature was essentially oral and depended on recitation and oral communication. This made memory an important art. It was so important that Greek teachers of wisdom gave it foremost consideration in their instruction. The principles of memory became one of the five basic divisions of the study of rhetoric, which also included proof, organization, style, and delivery. At the high point of rhetorical study the great Roman orator, Cicero, gave memory a place in his writings. A hundred years later, Quintilian summarized the best of classical instruction regarding memory. Almost all memory systems are based on organization of material by the use of artificial symbols. For example, Wally Minto, a modern teacher of techniques to better use your mind, gives a series of words that rhyme with numbers: one, bun; two, shoe; three, gee; four, core; five, dive; six, mix; seven, leaven; eight, weight; nine, pine; and ten, bin. If you were remembering a shopping list, you would picture each item with the memory cue word. You might picture yourself eating a bun filled with cheese, a shoe with a box of soap in it, a dog sled with a bag of flour on it, a jar of peanut butter with an apple core in the top of it, and so on. Mr. Minto has taught his system of one hundred cue words to elementary school children. The children were able to improve their grades on social studies tests, which included knowing the names of presidents and many historical facts. Mr. Minto demonstrates how a good memory system is indispensable for success in any profession or business.

Divide the amount of time into 300 to find the number of words you speak per minute. Consider yourself a fast speaker if you read over 190 words per minute. A slow speaker reads about 120 words more or less per minute. Somewhere between 150 and 170 words per minute is used by those who are considered excellent speakers.

Another method is to compare the way you normally speak certain words with the way they sound if you purposely lengthened pronunciation. Try these words as you normally would say them.

get	mud	law	eat	lift	hat	set
tooth	teeth	loud	jug	door	house	sat
shoe	lie	eight	yes	six	caught	

Say them again, and this time, make them three seconds long. If you have no second hand to help you, say one-thousand-one, one-thousand-two, one-thousand-three, a few times, and you'll get a fair idea of what three seconds means. Of course, that is far too long for these words. It is important for you to notice whether you pronounced the middle sound in the word correctly the first time. By elongating the time used to pronounce certain words, you become more aware of their complete sound. Most of us cut words so short that the middle vowel sound becomes garbled. Say the next list of words aloud. If the pair of words sound exactly alike, you'll know for sure you are not giving the middle sound its correct length.

Yale — yell	peal — pill
shall — shell	deal — kill
tale — tell	wan — won
fail — fell	tar — tire
red — raid	food — feud
sail — sell	mood — mewed
dale — dell	Mary — merry — marry

If you pronounced any of the groups exactly alike, you will need to work more on learning accurate pronunciation of your vowels. We'll work more to clear up your articulation in another chapter. Right now, it's important to realize thoroughly that speed sometimes kills a word. It causes confusion with other words and stops your word from having its full impact.

When you were a small child, you repeated and lengthened words you liked. Sometimes it was the feel of the word — the way your tongue had to move around quickly to make each of the sounds in it (abracadabra). Sometimes it was the sound of the word (flip-flop). Sometimes it was the effect the word had on others that caused the impact (ass). See if you can recapture the fun of these words by giving each a full two-second length.

droopy	roar
lovely	glimmer
rustle	lonely
crash	grumble
snowflake	sluttish
stroll	fluffy
gloomy	luscious
merry	passion
hush	happy
sputter	murmur

stretch	moan
lover	delicious
grisly	rumble
morbid	

Lengthening a word and thoroughly enjoying it is a part of your voice power. Not only does it add interest to your speech, it helps to convey the depth of your meaning to another.

Words that give us very precise information are often short and vivid. They give as much character to speech as long, emphasized words. Slowing these words down wrecks their impact. If you are a slow speaker, repeat the list using about one quarter of a second for each word.

flick	glib
tip	snap
clip	nit
flip	chip
snit	pip
blip	fib
flit	dip
glint	bit
snip	click

Learning to vary the speed of speech to take advantage of both short and long words is one of the marks of full voice power. In the last few years "free speech" has been given a liberal interpretation and many four-letter words have become vogue. Some meetings are so punctuated by them that they no longer communicate any feeling, whether they are fast or slow! Finding fresh expressions in situations where there is no longer any bottom line for good taste is an intriguing challenge to anyone who has developed voice power.

Another timing characteristic that distracts is jerkiness. A jerk is a quick and suddenly arrested movement. It lacks coordination or rhythm, which in speech is usually very noticeable. An extreme example is stuttering. Our spoken language is very rhythmic with a regular recurrence of certain aspects or beats. We are so inherently rhythmic that we immediately react when it's missing. We live and depend upon rhythms. We eat, eliminate, breathe, sleep, and play regularly, and when we don't, over a period of time, we get sick. The biorhythm people tell us we have a twenty-three day physical rhythm, a twenty-eight day emotional rhythm, and thirty-three day intellectual rhythm. Most of us run our lives in a rhythmic fashion that includes five days of work, two days of something else, and then five more work days, and we can plot our rhythm for an entire month and find very little variation from month to month in our eating, sleeping, and working habits. Even our irregularities— the holidays, splurges, and crises—occur with systematic regularity. It isn't any wonder that we react with uneasiness to the person who speaks in spurts and jerks.

There is a way to more rhythmic speech for jerky speakers. By working on increasing consciousness of rhythm in every aspect of life, you can change your speech pattern. With hyperactive children who are delayed in developing speech and language, I introduce rhythmic speech patterns immediately. "What's in the box?" is a favorite. Every word has an equal stress as each word is spoken, and the box is hit. For adults, I develop a list of four-word sentences related to their lives and have them practice making each word the same length. By creating a rhythm with the sounds of words, they develop a basic sense of beat patterns. Once you have a feel for steady rhythm you can, like a drummer, experiment with variations. Feeling the rhythm inherent in speech is actually an awareness of the patterns of intensity. You can use the two lists of phrases and sentences in the chapter on loudness for rhythmic word practice.

In the old-time elocution schools, tapping, clapping, and beating sticks were sometimes used for stuttering and other speaking problems without long-lasting effects. These techniques may work with people who already have a well-developed sense of rhythm, but rhythmic people seldom have a problem of rhythm in speaking. I also find little carry-over from singing, tapping, and clapping to speech. My experience is similar to the results of some studies done at Stanford University. They demonstrated that training in separate sensory and physical skills was not as effective in improving speech as working on the speech and language directly.

You probably know stutterers can sing without stuttering. In fact, you probably have heard of at least one stutterer, Mel Tillis, who has a successful career in singing. Part of the reason for this is that other areas of the brain that function in singing are not primarily active in speaking. All the singing, tap dancing, and clapping in the world won't permanently relieve the unrhythmic speech of stuttering. In fact, I honestly have to say that I know of no technique that will permanently cure stuttering.

There is one process that helps and requires no therapy, and that's simply growing older. Many stutterers past forty-five say they rarely stutter, and when they do, they say it no longer upsets them. But don't despair if your problem in rhythm is stuttering, and you're far from the magic number. There are more therapies for stutterers than any other speech difficulty I know of, and many categories of professionals available to help. Recently, Bob Goldman and some other stutterers founded a national organization. More information on this project and where to go for help is in chapter 10.

No discussion of rhythm would be complete without reference to its use in poetry. Poetry touches off an appreciation for the rhythm of language and the feeling possible through it that transcends word choice and the arrangement of sounds. Here is a poem that shares the feelings experienced during a spring walk by a person who's just recovering from a serious illness. Read this exercise in life rhythm and language rhythm, and feel it blending with the rhythms of spring.

A stroll around Daffodil Hill — A wondrous walk devoid of talk
Filled with Nature's Words. A banty rooster stretches
His glistening neck and crows — announcing my coming.
An aged red barn greets me silently on my way. The old
Windmill whose turning fans were long ago by branches stopped
Monuments still its joy of once pumping water to the
Hillside greenery. Past the pink flowering plum, five white doves
Squat above their coves, and smoke-grey pigeons groom their feathers.

Unaware of the beauty of their message. Up the path
move my feet

Slowly as my eyes catch little surprises that peek from
pots

And tubs and barrels—rejoicing that Spring is here!
Hyacinths,

Crocuses, Violets—all gingerly unfolding blooms of
delicate hue

And I feel gloriously welcomed by their view. Around
the bend

And then full scene: Hills of daffodils nodding yellow
petals

Beneath the guarding branches of faithful Oaks still
grey from

Another season, now meet my face and I relax in their
bright

Company—recalling other days—now relinquished—
when

Children, friends and work controlled my crowded
thought-hours.

The whirring coo of an unseen peacock draws my eyes
to distant

Pines—green pointers to the cloudless blue of my New
Thought.

I slide onto a weathered bench and feel the rush of the
Fresh

Breeze fluffing my hair and scenting the air with Pine
and

Manzanita-mixed. The scuffling of children kicking
through brown

Oak leaves searching for acorns—treasure for their

pockets —

The yips of a puppy forbidden this walk — urge me on
my way

Down Daffodil Hill — counting the blooms tucked in
nests of

Fallen leaves and wondering still what their number
might be.

A rickety picket fence perched above a stone wall
shelters more

Growth along my path back. The remnants of Cones-
toga wagons

And rusting farm machines rest in contrast to the
newness of my

Spring — And I am glad for their reminder that Daffodils are

Forever New.

If you read the poem aloud, and poetry is written to be
read aloud, the dashes, commas, and periods guided the
timing. The significance of the timing became apparent
to you. Timing is also expressed in handwriting. It is
possible to interpret writing into a style of speaking by
using common indicators present in everyone's written
communication.

I have developed an exercise to help my voice power
students become more aware of the timing in their own
speech through their handwriting. They write about a
recent incident in which they did not say what they would
have liked to have said, using a variety of dashes, dots,
and punctuation of their own invention. Next, they
interpret characteristics of the writing that show how they
would have said the passage aloud. Although the inter-

pretations are not standard and students often have their own meanings for characteristics, certain interpretations occur frequently. Intensity is indicated by the pressure of the pencil. Flourishes, curlicues, and circled dots over the "i's" suggest a slow rate; incompletely formed letters and no embellishments suggest a faster rate. Very small writing is equated with softness and very large writing with excessive loudness. Variety in pitch is indicated by the inconsistencies in the height of letters and writing first on, then above or below, the lines. A dash is a signal to take a quick, deep breath. Several dots in a row have suggested an "ahh" or "err." The students suggest meanings for other creative punctuation. Word spacing indicates pacing. Little space means even pacing, and a variety of spacing means many changes in pacing, perhaps building to a climax.

After the symbols have been interpreted, the students read their own compositions using these guidelines. Next, the exercise is carried one step further. The students write about an exciting moment in their lives, and they read each other's aloud following the agreed-upon guidelines.

Frequently the whole concept of timing becomes clear to a student when a composition is read according to the cues to interpretation provided through his or her handwriting.

Letting yourself pause and allowing others their silent periods during a conversation has a priceless value in full voice power. Many people who maintain a steady pace do not seem to believe in pauses. I remember one client whose lifestyle reflected an unrelenting pace. Her day was one great big job of being a supermom. She also insisted and planned everything so that her husband was a superdad. They attended all the school meetings; taxied their kids to Scouts, singing, dancing, skating, riding lessons, church activities; and had specific times for each child individually every day. There was no pause in the determination to make the "family together" idea work. Her conversation showed the same pattern as her life "I don't have time to think!" was her most frequent comment. When she came for help, for chronic hoarseness, she did not like my leisurely pace and even tried to speed *me* up.

Pacing in communication very frequently reflects the pace you keep in your life. Once you're aware of your pacing pattern, you can choose to vary it. One good reason not to work hard, play hard, talk with consistent intensity, and keep up the same pace is your need for a varied pace in body and mind in order to maintain health. "Burn out" is the latest catch-phrase for the person who no longer cares about what happens in his job. Of course, Dr. Joyce Brothers and other psychologists who are treating the burn-out syndrome in workshops across the country have many complex explanations for disinterested behavior found in many civil service occupations as well other jobs. Perhaps burn-out may be the way the body and the mind react to intensity in pacing that never seems to pay off in personal satisfaction. So take a long look at your pacing in speaking and see whether you need some variety in more places than just what comes out of your mouth.

The pause is the natural divider of your phrases. If you already are a pauser, maybe you add an "uh" or "er" in between thoughts just to make sure your listener knows you aren't stopping. One friend of mine always made a "pss, pss, pss" in his pauses and sometimes used it as a "starter." Recently I've been told of two other professionals who use the same sound as "place holders." Maybe the combined lip and tongue action feels better than the dreary jaw drop for "uh," but I've heard that both of these men are mimicked by fellow employees. Reading aloud is a good way to begin to eliminate this infectious habit. The daily newspaper is ideal reading matter. The columns help you to see in a glance what the natural phrasing might be, and there are plenty of punctuation marks for pause indicators. Many newspapers use a style that includes many direct quotes that give you a chance to vary your pacing. Buy one *National Enqurier*, and you'll have enough good practice material from their human interest stories for weeks. Carefully written to hold your attention, the *Enquirer* stories contain a variety of punctuation devices including the great communicative pause, the dash.

If you don't like their stories, read aloud the advertisements. Although the style of some ads may seem ludicrous, it does provide the opportunity for exaggerated practice of pausing, phrasing, and pacing with a relaxed attitude.

A relaxed body and mind will help you read aloud using all of the facets of voice power you have learned so far. "Rupture agony disappears" and "Away with those curlers! Now at long last a permanent wave that lasts . . . and lasts by just combing your hair" may give you the exact relaxed feeling you'll need for quality, the sound essence of you. In the next chapter, you'll learn additional techniques to improve your voice quality.

SEVEN

Voice Quality,
Your Sound Essence

The nuance that makes each voice different from all other voices is its quality. This elusive part of voice is sometimes described as tone color and is credited with giving away our hidden attitudes. It is the part of voice on which many of our intuitions about honesty, kindness, and intentions of others are based. It transcends the sum of its parts (pitch, resonance, loudness, timing, and diction) and communicates all the shades of feeling between subtle empathy and indifference.

Although tone color is the way we modulate all the aspects of voice quality to express our reactions it is not responsible for our basic individual sound. Basic sound or timbre is composed of a fundamental frequency and a large number of overtones. The fundamental is the consistent lowest sound used in a voice. The overtones above the fundamental vary in number, frequency, and intensity, and it is impossible to hear any single overtone clearly. It is these overtones that we will learn to modify as we pull together the voice power elements worked with so far. To achieve acceptable or outstanding quality does not require an understanding of the perfect balance among breathing, pitch, resonance, timing, loudness and articulation, but only a development of an awareness of the degree of emotional color added to every spoken word. By exploring emotional color we will gain a better feel for what the physical voice structures do to create emotional expression. Through specific exercises with these structures, we will learn to teach them to work as effectively as possible to produce tone colors that represent the self we want to project. For some that may mean cold objectivity. For others, warmth and friendliness. Either is possible for all basic timbres.

Voice quality begins with basic timbre, and like basic body type, it has not been dramatically altered by any of the current therapeutic approaches except surgery and reconstruction techniques. Basic timbre is created by the shape, size, mass, and placement of your lungs, larynx, pharynx, and nasal chambers. It is also dynamically influenced by the health of these structures, which is in your control. Congested lungs, irritated vocal folds, and clogged nasal and sinus passages distort basic timbre. Unless you take responsibility for keeping your voice-producing tissue and the resonating pathways above and below them as healthy as possible, you will never know your basic timbre.

The first steps for attaining health given in chapter 2 emphasized care of the total body including techniques to improve circulation, assist assimilation, provide rest, and encourage elimination. Chapter 11 will provide further techniques and motivating information to reinforce your decision to embark on a care program. When your total body is healthy, you'll find it easier to apply what you know about pitch, resonance, loudness, and timing to supporting and enhancing your basic timbre. Good posture and correct use of breath support it. Your natural pitch is a basic element in it, tone placement for good resonance builds it, sufficient loudness accentuates it, but without adequate timing, the synergy caused by combining all elements will not work fully. The clarity of clean articulation is also a vital part of timbre, and we will begin working on those sounds especially essential for quality later in this chapter. These sounds, predominantly vowels, are also responsible for emotional color.

You must decide what kind of tone color you want. It is your essence and can be built by carefully developing the voice elements learned in the preceding chapters — natural pitch, good resonance, correct breathing, good timing, and a variety of loudness and intensity. You will also need to enrich your understanding and use of emotion in your voice.

Psychologists report that the emotion we express with our voice arouses similar emotions in others. People think words can hide their feelings at the moment, but their voices telegraph their emotions. People who know the impact of emotional coloring take a few moments to make sure their voices will express their words. A cold, aloof voice makes the most genuine attempts to be friendly ring insincere. Often, those who are new at being authoritative incorporate chilliness into their voices without realizing they are defeating their purpose. Studies have shown that the cold, authoritarian boss is frequently and purposefully sabotaged by employees who cannot identify with or feel loyalty to an impersonal figurehead. Stealing from the inventory produces no guilt at all. On the other hand, studies have shown that one characteristic of winners in every area of life is the ability to maintain a relaxed, friendly mood regardless of stress.

Reacting in this way is a learned behavior that requires purposeful, continuous practice. However, the reward of personal emotional growth far outweighs the discomfort felt when you begin to practice control of emotional color in your voice. You will be able to turn some relationships completely around and make all of your interactions flow more slowly once you decide to take full responsibility for your own success through using your voice coloring to convey good feelings. Even if your message is a criticism or an unpleasant announcement, your voice coloring can awaken cooperation instead of furnishing fuel for hostility and sabotaging actions. The coloring begins in your own head.

Color your target person warm in your thinking. Do it by picturing the iceberg smiling or picturing him or her greeting you with a big hug. If you are one of the very few who cannot imagine people in your head or fantasize scenes when you close your eyes, you'll need to work more with thoughts and words. Drawing pictures of the person's face—circles with eyes, nose, smiling mouth, and so on—will do. Scotch tape them around where you will see them, and be reminded of your warm friend-to-be. Whenever you glance at the picture, think or say something warm about the person. Try "you're nice," or simply, "I like you." Sometimes say, "You're very helpful to me." Usually that is true! Someone who motivates you to want to be his or her friend is really helping you to expand your ways of thinking and doing by helping you learn to use the conscious and subconscious mind.

Much recent psychological and medical research indicates thoughts don't just stay in the mind. They are a form of energy that travels outward and can be transmitted to others. *Medical World News*, the *Life* magazine of the medical profession, carried an article about Olga Worrell, who is able to change blood pressure, temperature, and pulse rate in another's body with thoughts she directs toward that individual. Doctors demonstrated on a national television program, how Olga could create these changes even while she was some distance from the patient. Instruments documented the patient's improvement. Similar findings have been discussed at medical conferences across the country, with physicians, psychologists, and physicists of national stature reporting the same kinds of evidence regarding the potency of thought.

By doing the simple exercise described, you not only change your way of thinking about a person, but you are actually building up an atmosphere conducive to fostering a friendship. As you feel a bond being created between you, you can then encourage it further by extending a casual invitation to have coffee or whatever else you use for an ice breaker. Given exposure to heartfelt warmth in thought and considerate acts, even the coldest, scariest voice should gradually thaw as well as the human wearing it.

If you feel that you may be the person who has a cold voice, you can change it if it suits your purposes. If you do, it will probably increase your circle of friends. But examiné your motives for having projected a chilly voice in the first place; changing your emotional color could also be counterproductive, as in Alberta's case.

Alberta considers herself efficient, objective, and

competent in her job and relationships with others. She has no family in the vicinity and generally avoids close contacts because she does not want other people taking time from her solitary hobbies, which are painting, sewing, and creating mosaics. She claims she is comfortably happy. If she added warmth to her matter-of-fact voice and became more open and friendly, she would probably see her life-style changing to include more socialization. Her efficiency might slip if she allowed her attention to be drawn to others; it's very hard to file, phone, and figure correctly if you're concerned about someone's divorce, children's illnesses, and the new man just hired. "Perhaps," she says, "I might no longer be objective about those working near me. Then I might be forced to seek a new job at the age of forty. Since I'm satisfied with my job and certainly do not view my life-style as destructive, I may not want to make the leap to more expansive living. Not only expansive—it could be expensive. Lunching out with others, entertaining at home, new clothes to go with the experiences, maybe even a higher telephone bill could punch a large hole in my art supply budget. In the long run, I might not have as many happy moments if I choose change."

Alberta's life-style is a matter of choice and she uses the aloofness in her voice to achieve her desired goal. Aloof or chilly emotional color can be used even more selectively than Alberta does in avoiding contact with people, such as in dealing with unsolicited salesmen. However, if you do feel that your voice is putting off people you would like to know better, you will want to learn to manipulate it so that you can be warm when you want to be.

The first step is to understand what cool quality is. One of its most important components is tension. Tension narrows and restricts the number of voice tones. Try clenching your jaw while saying coldly, "Who are you?" Your pitch should immediately change. The cold voice is usually flat, dull, and lifeless. If emotion comes through, it is often on the unpleasant, rejecting side, even if the actual intent is only to be aloof or dignified. I often see a certain deliberateness in the individual with the frost-bit voice. The old-style manager was the epitomy of deliberate coldness. Dagwood Bumstead's boss, Mr. Dithers, is, of course, a parody of this, and Lou Grant and Kojak occasionally give us glimpses of cold, deliberate voice personalities. The Godfather was the ultimate in coldness, and some of us still shiver when we imagine his voice.

The cold voice can be a cover-up for weakness and insecurity or a disguise for a calculated need to control other people, another symptom of a basically poorly functioning human being. But often, as in people like Alberta, it's a purposeful life choice, and everything else seems to fall in line with that choice. The choice not to be involved carries over into voice quality, but once it's a habit and the muscles have learned certain tensions to produce the pitch, resonance, tongue, and jaw responses, this pattern must be replaced through specific exercises to reinforce new learning.

A brilliant, confident voice quality, one that rings with truth and authority, is desired as much as a warm one. When I asked for specific examples of this quality, men chose Walter Cronkite, Richard Burton, and Sargent Shriver, with Adlai Stevenson and Franklin Roosevelt as runners-up. The brilliant, confident ring was praised by men and women in the voices of Texas congresswoman Barbara Jordan, British actress Glenda Jackson, former California congresswoman Yvonne Braithwaite Burke, ambassador to Great Britain Anne Armstrong, and former stars Loretta Young and Lorraine Day. It isn't just luck that gave them those voices. Luck involves only about 2 percent of good voice quality and the rest is work; the same ratio that Thomas Edison described for genius operated for these voice powers. The luck, of course, is having the structures for a good basic timbre. The 98 percent includes maintaining health in these structures, seeking training in speaking, and using every opportunity that comes along to use the voice. When I asked four other speech pathologists what they thought was the outstanding feature of brilliant voices, the reply was resonance and clarity of articulation. Both are well within your attainment.

If your voice is throaty, you might just want less guttural quality, rather than a brilliant, ringing clarity. In order to achieve your goal, you need to understand how your voice quality developed and what maintains it.

For John, his father was his voice model. The chin was always down and a stern, deep voice commanded five active boys to keep the chores up. Without consciously realizing what was happening, John adopted his father's head carriage. Although he disliked his father's gruffness and rigidity, inwardly he admired his father's strength and disciplined nature. Although he sees his father only during holidays and still does not tolerate the elder man's continued dominance over the family, he has so many of his voice and posture characteristics that it is easy to identify them as father and son.

If you push your jaw firmly down and say, "Alabama, Alamo, and Arkansas," you will feel the tension in the back of the tongue and tightness in the back of the throat. That same tightness extends further down the throat in the vocal folds and limits their flexibility. All of the muscle tightness constricts the resonating cavities, muffling the sound and keeping the pitch too low. The lips move very little, so the sound lacks the clarity of oral resonance or any hum from the "m's," "n's," and "ing's." When you think of the muscle work necessary to hang on to that pattern, you come to feel that the cure must be easier than the disease.

The throaty, harsh voice is even more noticeable when it's coming from a female body. The rough quality in women is sometimes called "smoker's voice," and studies have shown that persistent smoking does dry the voice tissues. A narrow band of tones is sometimes the devastating result for an otherwise attractive woman. Many women strive for a lower voice than is natural and end up with chronic hoarseness. Still others want a breathy, little girl voice, and of course, must give up some clarity in articulation and some variety in loudness and pitch changes in order to achieve and maintain it. Those who have the little girl voice not by choice get rather tired of being told to ask Mommy to come to the phone. Consistently being mistaken for a male on the phone can also become irritating.

The famous British actor Sir John Guilgud was interviewed on a popular morning news program. Said the interviewer, "I've heard that when you begin working on a new role, you start by studying feet, the way the character is to walk or move."

"No, no," denied Guilgud, "I always start with the voice. That is the most important part of any role."

The key to developing effective voice quality is in recognizing the different roles you play in the course of a day. They may include spouse, parent, employee, employer, friend, lover, consumer, salesperson, and so on. Each role focuses on a different combination of personality traits, thereby requiring different voice images. Irritation with a lover is not usually expressed in the same way as annoyance with a store clerk. However, often people who have image problems are those who cannot alter the quality of their voices to match their various roles. They speak to everyone in the same voice.

In order to express exactly the quality you want in any one role, you must first be able to identify how you currently speak.

For starters, pick a minor role in which you find yourself often. Shopper is a good one. As you talk to the store personnel — sales clerks, cashiers — listen carefully to how their voices sound. When you hear something that sounds like a quality problem, such as light, wispy, breathy voice or raspiness, consider how their lips and jaw are moving. It is not uncommon that when you hear bad quality, the lips are barely moving, the jaw is not relaxed, or they both are held in a strange position. Mouth movement can greatly enhance quality. Start with some mouth exercises to loosen your lips.

For the first exercise, rest a few fingers lightly on your lips, take a deep breath, and say "puh, puh, puh, puh," until you run out of air. One of my students said she substituted her boyfriend's cheek for her fingers and still captured the intent of the exercise — lip movement combined with tactile kinesthesia (muscle feedback). Another student looked at her a bit strangely and asked, "Did Joe shave off his beard?"

"No," replied the first student, "you really notice lip movement when you're kissing a brush!" The incident grew into my "brush kissing" lip technique to teach lip awareness. A gentle brush used usually for cuticles or face is quite effective, but hardier souls have used any brush that was available.

Lip movement is something so taken for granted, it's really difficult to get back in touch with it again. Do the brush technique once a day for a while to best train your lips. Hold the brush close to your lips without actually touching them. As you make the "puh" sound, they must pucker enough to touch the brush and then relax. "Puh" is a silent sound and should contain only air and lip movement, enabling concentration on the feel of the movement without getting the sound-making folds involved. After practicing "puh" for a while, add some sound to the exercise, incorporating another quality qualifier, the "ah" sound. Say "ah, puh, ah, puh, ah, puh," and don't forget to touch the brush on the "puh" part, and make sure your jaw is really opening on the "ah" part. Use an inch-and-a-match to check whether your jaw comes open enough, but be gentle with yourself and don't strain your jaw to open wider than is fairly comfortable. If you hear all sorts of clicks and noises, it isn't a rusty jaw, but a rather common problem in our country, called temporal mandibular joint syndrome. In chapter 11, I'll tell you how and where to find help or an evaluation of your noisy jaw situation, and all the things that go with it. Correction takes r_oney, time, treatment, and patience, and there's nothing to be done to help the process except to learn to be aware of stress, muscle tension, and relaxation. You learn more about that with every exercise that you do in this book.

The gentle change from one type of sound to another cultivates quality. Try "ah, puh, buh; ah, puh, buh." Repeat it about ten times. The vowel "ah" relaxes the throat and helps the muscles to move easily into the succeeding positions. All of the other vowels play a major role in developing clear quality. Vowel sounds are not just restricted to "a," "e," "i," "o," and "u," we actually use more than twenty vowel sounds in daily speech. Take a few minutes to verify your vowels to make sure you produce the subtle differences that beautify basic timbre. Pronounce the bold vowel sounds exactly the same in the following:

hat, plaid, pat, tan, lather, back, nanny, glad, sad, mad, dad

I call this the "jaw lip" sound because it can't be formed without jaw and lip movement. It is effective in stimulating movement in the mouth. Next, feel the jaw drop as you say this next series of words.

father, arm, sergeant, hearth, offer, balm, shop, tot, dark, guard, clock, not, hot, odd

If you want to practice further, look for the "a" with the two dots over it in the dictionary. The mouth opening should be about one full inch. If you want

122

make a matchstick measure to help retrain your lips and jaw.

Next, in importance to "ah" in uplifting quality is the short "e" sound in these words.

if, it, big, city, live, will, this, been, busy, women, build, fit, rid, slip, quick, lip, sit kid, going, seeing, having

It is one of the sounds that is quite distinctive in our language, though so frequently buried by distortion. In some languages, this sound does not exist; in others it is heard only occasionally so that students who learned these other languages first rarely learn to use it correctly. If you lengthen the short "e" sound, it becomes another vowel. The resulting accent may resemble that of a Spanish immigrant with him becoming heem; this, theez; and give, geeve.

Another vowel sound, the short "a," is often totally absent from the speech of people living in rural western communities. Emphasize the short "a" in the following words to verify that you use it consistently. The best word to practice with is the first one:

yes, step, ten, leg, press, next, length, fresh, egg, end, edge, send, head, best, dress, bed, men, let, rest, leather, many, tell, bed

These little words used over and over in daily speech are the ones that give the most trouble in improving this sound. I still slip back into the habit of agreeing with a "yeah," whenever I'm with someone else who does. I tried switching completely to "true," but found I was adding clout to statements I really was not all that sure of.

"True" is an excellent example of the next vowel to verify for a consistent quality in voice power. Because it does require mouth movement accuracy, we tend to slight it, falling short of the sound that forces the lips to go fully outward. I often help children learn this sound by using my thumb and second finger to help the lips come in for the pucker. You might find this tactile approach in front of a mirror will help regain your "ooo." Here are some practice words I like.

moon, croon, tune, loon, boost, rooster, lampoon, groom, boon, jewel, swoon, plume, schooner, swoop, droop, scoop, loop, truth, superstitious, maneuver, fruit, canoe, grew, troupe

The resonance for this sound is kept right in the mouth area and the tongue fully shapes the breeze of air across it.

For the next quality vowel sound, there is a complete switch. Now, you must pucker in reverse. All but two students in my last voice class cut short this combination vowel sound. With just a bit more duration, this sound adds a great clarity to many words used every day. Give your lips a little pull outward as you say the sound to help them get the expansive feel. Good practice words:

find, buy, night, aisle, eye, ice, tie, sky, hide, tight, might, right, pipe, nine, shine, type, slide, like, fire, tire, bite, mice, wide, file, ideal, item, iron, bye, fly, high, my, guide, tide, why, guy, try, shy, spy, die, pride, five, kind, time, line, wise.

The dictionary marks this sound with a dash over a small "i" if you want to look for more words to practice.

You've already discovered that for some of the most important quality vowel sounds, your jaw must move. Jawing can mean more than a nagging tongue. Using a chewing movement puts many of the muscles involved in creating quality into perfect relationship. Chewing can also sweeten sound quality. Start off with a few bites of "chew-chaw" in front of the mirror. As you repeat "chew-chaw" twenty times, notice that your tongue as well as your jaws and lips are in constant motion, Next, try these words.

choose, poaching, scratch, time, ashes, porch, matches, chosen, charity, peach, chalice, butcher, latch, choose, pitch, chip, recharge, search, chill, peach, blow, each, agile

This is the only kind of chewing guaranteed to reduce your weight. Now, with lots of jaw movement, try these full sentences.

The child reached cautiously to touch the teacher's chalk.
Charley had a cheap lunch of chili on the beach.
Our rich orchard has many choice cherry trees along the beach side of our ranch.
Each of us has watched the church bell chime and greeted our righteous preacher cheerfully.
Please take this cheap chipped picture to the kitchen and throw it into the trash carrier

cheerfully.

Mitchell, the merchant, formerly the butcher, remains a rich bachelor and was too cheap to purchase each of us a lunch at the Anxious Grape Restaurant.

"The child's speech was challenging," says the righteous speech therapist.

Charley Chan lit a match and searched for the ancient watch in the chilly Exchange.

We watched for a chance to catch his touchy teacher munching on chips and chocolates for lunch.

Of course, you won't have much use for those sentences; they were composed of sounds that would naturally make your jaw move. Now say the fifty most used words in the English language moving your jaws and chewing. These are the fifty words used most often by college men in almost six hundred speeches studied by speech scientists.

the, and, of, to, a, in, that, is, it, you, they, this, we, have, are, was, be, he, for, on, I, there, one, or, will, but, as, all, with, has, go, at, our, which, by, not, were, had, from, his, very, what, now, would, up, about, if, out, when, can

Since the object of these exercises is to retrain old habits, it is critical to use these little words in phrases. Adding increased jaw movement in a natural way is an important step to master.

Unfortunately, jaw movement is very unpopular because many people feel very self-conscious when they first begin. They feel they're all mouth. Remember this is just practice, so try chewing these phrases, letting it be okay for you to be "all mouth." Try to keep your jaws moving, and they don't have to be open widely.

Why didn't you go? Where have you been? Did you see that? Why did he go? What did he say? What did I tell you? How are you? Do you want me to? How about you? You ought to ask! Aren't you coming? We'll take care of it. We asked them to stop. They couldn't have stopped him. Isn't that interesting? They can go anywhere. That's the way it goes. That's a lot of cars. See if you can. Not if I can help it. Now more than ever. I wish I could. Let me see. It's been so long. I don't want to stay. I don't know. He's one of the best. Give me a little time. Go on outside. Give it to them. Get off of here. As far as I can tell.

Another quality problem is a weak, thin sound. More push is needed to put muscle behind it. When you make the muscles in your arms work by pushing, the vocal folds also work. They come together more firmly and the tone is clearer and better. The breathy, weak voice may be the failure of weak vocal muscles to come together completely. Do this experiment and see if your voice improves with push-ups that are similar to the cobra posture in yoga. Lay on your stomach and put your hands under your chest. Raise your chest slowly off the floor as you say "I like meat, toast, fruit, and juice." Now let yourself collapse and repeat the sentence from the collapsed position. Now say it again as you rise, and listen carefully. Every sound will be stronger and clearer. Try it a few more times to really tune in the quality. Then stand up. Try to get the same quality without the push-up. If you can't come close, hit the floor again for more practice.

If you rise slowly and come down just as slowly, you'll feel a relaxing effect throughout the entire body. The stretching of the spine and alternate tensing and relaxing of muscles in this slow movement results in an immediate renewal of energy. You won't wear yourself out by taking a firmer hold on quality through this exercise.

The next exercise requires more push and utilizes the maximum gluteus muscle, adding more pressure through the weight of your buttocks. Sit down on the floor, clasp your hands under your knees, and rock backward, bringing the feet over your head so that the knees rest on your forehead. Now say, "Tomorrow may be the day I receive money in the afternoon mail." Rock forward and repeat the sentence in the sitting position. Now bottoms up again and repeat the sentence, listening closely for a difference in resonance as well as quality. If the sound is a little too heavy for you, flip over on your stomach, do the cobra again, say the sentence, and see if you like that quality better. It should be lighter and clearer, simply because there is less pressure exerted by the muscles in your vocal folds and other muscles and, of course, the position is less these. If both of these are impossible for you because of size, shape, or disposition, here's one you can do without leaving your chair. The change in quality will not be as dramatic, but you will hear a difference.

Clasp your fingers together and push your hands against each other as hard as you can. Repeat the sentence as you push. If you can't exert sufficient pressure to cause a change in voice, try pushing down on the arms of a chair as you repeat the sentence. One client of mine could lift himself completely off the chair using just his arms and then would attain a complete change in quality from a light, weak voice to a strong, resonant baritone.

If you absolutely refuse exercise in any size, shape, or form; buy a tube-type vibrator. It won't strengthen like the push-up, but it will help. It is not necessary to pay more by buying one from a dealer in adult personal supplies; the vibrators found in joke and magic shops are cheaper and work just as well.

The whole idea of using a vibrator is to stimulate more muscle activity in the vocal folds. First put the tip right on your chin bone with a firm pressure. Read these sentences:

Watch out. Be quiet. I see. Why not? Look out! Have fun. Don't worry. Stay a while. Go away. Come here. I'm tired. Do it! Hurry up. Help me. Come in. Come again. Don't go.

You felt the extra vibration in your jaw bone, and should also hear the added vibration in your speech. I always feel a tickle in my ears. Ticklish people may take a while to get accustomed to the feeling of vibrator vibes. Put the vibrator under the chin and say these sentences slowly so that you can hear as well as feel the muscle stimulation.

I am fine. Please come again. Another cup of coffee? Pass the bread. What a pretty flower. It's a hot day. I'm thirsty. You are late. Don't do it. Please help me. Shut the door. Open the window. You drive the car. I take the bus. Read the mail. Buy some milk. Get some bread. Where are my shoes? I can't come. Answer the phone. Take time to talk. Check and see.

With the vibrator pointed under the chin you should have felt and heard scratchy quality that time. That's the kind of voice you wouldn't want permanently, and this stimulation will help prevent that. Watch it lessen as you do this next exercise. Put the tip of the vibrator directly on your Adam's apple, that bone that protrudes from your neck. It's part of the protective covering of the delicate vocal folds. Now say one of these sentences with the vibrator directly on that bone. Then repeat the same sentence *after removing it*.

She'll find out soon. Are you coming in? How many cars are there? What day is it? They will be here. Can he cook? Are they different? Did he do it? What do you want? Come again, won't you? He isn't working, is he? He was sick, wasn't he? I'm going home, but I'll be back. Isn't she finished? You can go if I can. You can go if she can't. Are you still sick? Is she really lonely or bored? Who cares? I do.

Your voice quality should have been much improved when you removed the vibrator. The relaxation induced by the vibration as well as the improved muscle function are responsible for this improvement. This gentle stimulation of the muscles also increases the blood supply. Continue with the vibrator by tucking it sideways under your jaw, saying a sentence, removing it, and repeating it.

The nerves that serve your tongue can also be perked up by using the vibrator. I discovered this in my work with cerebral palsied and cleft palate clients who had poor control of their tongues. With better range of movement, more flexibility, and coordination, articulation was much clearer. Indeed, I learned long ago that poor articulation takes much longer to correct without physical stimulation. It can't hurt you in any case, and it will give your tongue tip some increased zip. The same goes for lagging lips. Moving your vibrator around them will help them to move quickly. Remember, intermittent stimulation is better than a constant pressure. If you carefully listen to both sentences — one with the vibrator and one without it — you will also develop a quality-finding ear.

After you've learned the difference in qualities, you're ready to try using a tape recorder during practice. If you don't have one, you can speak into a tube. (An empty toilet paper or towel roll will do.) The tube will capture your voice, making it sound louder. You will notice your good voice habits as well as your bad ones. Later it will help you get ready to practice, and whenever you pick it up, you'll feel like you're set for something different to happen.

First try to achieve a soft, weak, gentle oral quality while recording the following paragraph. Keep resonance to a bare minimum by holding the sound right in your mouth. The tone should be shallow and confined with few variations in loudness or pitch.

I'm sorry to hear that. I wish I could do something to help you. You know how it is with my job, and mother, and my car problems. This just isn't a good time for me. I know you'll work it out. You always do. Why don't you call me in a week or so and we can get together and talk over coffee.

Play it back and listen for gentleness, softness, and weakness. If you hear nothing that even resembles those emotions, be still a moment. Think of some time in your life when you were deeply affected by sorrow. Read it again and see if that emotional color can be expressed in your voice. Listen to the replay carefully to see if you hear gentleness expressed through your voice.

If you still feel you are not expressing that tone, it probably is lacking in your voice color repertoire. You may very likely be out of touch with that gentle, soft part of you, a part we all have, a part that needs expression in the voice. If you can put it into your voice, you can put it into your life. There are always times for gentleness and softness. This is a different kind of voice power, and one that may not typically portray you.

Another oral quality that may not be in your daily repertoire is the tremulous voice. It is a voice quality that usually comes unbidden, yet the wavering, tremulous voice is a masterpiece of resonance force and emotional color. You may hear this quality in an ailing elderly person or in a person troubled by great uncertainty in some problem. Sometimes it's almost crying. Try to recall a time when you were so shaken by some unusual happening that you could scarcely talk. See if

132

you can get in touch with that voice color as you read and record the next paragraph.

I just feel like I can't stand another minute of it. It's the same old pattern over and over again. He makes all kinds of promises. I make the same demands, and I feel rotten about doing it. I just wish he could change, but he can't. You can't help but feel sorry for him. But how, in God's name, can you help him?

As you listened to that tone color, you may have said, "I can do without that one!" But at some time in your life drama, you may either use it or hear it. If you're in touch with that tape, you'll recognize it and know that this role we all play at some time can be altered when we decide to do it. The circumstances do not have to change, but we do and so does the emotional color in our voice quality.

For contrast, play the role of the leader and use what we call "full quality." This is the tone color heard in voices that have great dignity, superior confidence, and a command over the situation. You might hear it in your minister's voice, or a favorite congressman's, or in the hero's or heroine's voice on your favorite daytime soap opera. I remember hearing it in an old-time radio program, "Mr. District Attorney." The announcer said, "Champion of the people, guardian of our fundamental rights, to life, liberty, and the pursuit of happiness." Full quality requires full use of breath power. You'll need all the volume and resonance you can muster. The timing needs to be a bit slower than that you'd generally use in a public speech. Record this and then listen for your full quality. Your voice should be really big and impressive.

> We come here to ask you to consider our needs as human beings. We need first of all, enough food for our children. We do not care about ourselves, but our children must not suffer because we have no money, no jobs, and nothing to offer them, but our love. We know the American ethic to be one of generosity and kindness to those in trouble. We come to you, our last hope, to beseech you to grant us the opportunity you have offered others who came to your shores.

Full voice quality should be a goal if you are entering the political arena or any position that requires presentations before large audiences. Your tape recorder, your ability to imagine yourself as a leader of people, and your willingness to work with the exercises in resonance, loudness, and timing will boost you to full voice quality.

If you're just interested in what I call best natural quality, it's not going to take nearly the amount of work that full quality requires. Work on breathing until you can change the fullness and loudness of your tones easily. Understand what your natural pitch is and practice until it's a habit. Watch your resonance and steer it toward balance. (You don't want all oral resonance, all nasal, or all pharyngeal resonance.) Best natural quality has a warmth and genuine flavor that reflects a healthy body and cooperating mind. It reflects another quality I call spirit. Consciousness is a synonym for spirit; in some dictionaries, energy is too. This means that your best natural voice reflects the very best of you, in terms of what you really are, and what you can be as a human being.

The next chapter delves further into helping you create a voice quality that is truly an expression of you.

EIGHT

Expressive
Intonation and
Emphasis

The melody of your speaking voice can be unforgettable. Every time a person speaks, the words are a tune. Capitalizing on this discovery, Bell Telephone is developing an infallible identification system. Sophisticated instruments will encode the exact intonation and emphasis pattern of each individual. Acoustically each of us has a precise pattern of frequencies and intensities that even a skilled impersonator cannot duplicate.

Although our brains have sensitive voice identification mechanisms, most of us never develop the ability to identify specific voice differences, nor do most people vary their own voices. Most voices blend easily into a monotonous mass, with only an occasional voice having a memorable melody. The intonation of any sentence can be recorded by writing below each word a note on a staff, like a song. Say, "Hello, my name is Jimmy Carter and I'm running for president." Which of the notations in the illustration is closer to the way you would have spoken that now famous introduction?

Good speakers sometimes use as many as twenty-five different notes to give variety and meaning to their

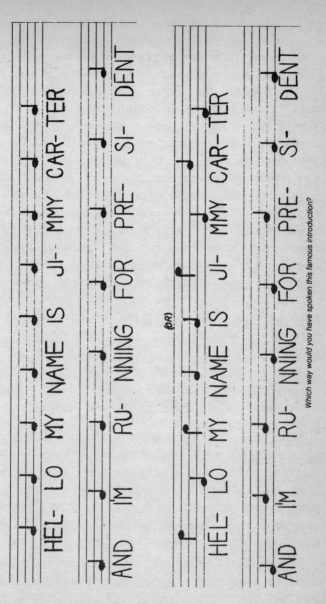

Which way would you have spoken this famous introduction?

137

words. Most of us use a much smaller range. Speakers who use only one note are quite tedious to listen to. If you expand your use of pitch to include just five different notes, your voice power will dramatically improve. Intonation patterns will become vivid and your voice will flow with interest.

Most people do not realize they consistently use intonation patterns in their speech. These sound patterns are encoded in the brain and are used by everyone under similar circumstances. Although the frequencies and intensities still differ, the general up and down melody in the voice remains similar for people of the same language. If you read these frequently used comments with the intonation pattern that is marked, you'll experience this.

When the line is at the base of the letters, read it in your usual pitch. When the line is above the word, say it on a higher pitch. Remember to keep each whole word on the *same* pitch.

What is the ⌐matter?
How are you ⌐feeling?
Why is he angry?

That kind of pattern gives a strange feeling of incompleteness. English-speaking people learn to drop the voice at the end of sentences except for special cases. When a person unacquainted with our language doesn't obey our intonation rules, we're puzzled. Sometimes we'll repeat, or parrot, what was said. The foreigner will think we're acknowledging that the translation is accurate, although he or she is probably sure the right words were *selected*. By not dropping their voices at the end of sentences, these people unsuspectingly lead you to expect more to be said. Intonation patterns establish a tone of certainty and completeness.

To use intonation, you must use a major principle of emphasis. That means simply that you'll usually raise your pitch on the word that is most important in the sentence. It is an automatic action learned in the cradle. Watch how you automatically follow my intonation patterns below in order to make the right meaning clear in spite of the exact similarity in sound. A line above the word raises its pitch: below it, lowers it; the vertical connecting lines indicate a change in pitch will come on the next word.

> The sheep herd will move, deer.
> The sheep herd will move deer?
> The sheep heard Will move deer.
> The sheep herd will move, Dear.
> The sheep heard Will move, Dear.

Intonation patterns guide us intuitively to understanding meaning even when we can only guess at what someone with a severe speech problem or a regional accent is saying. Pitch patterns frequently shift up and down in the middle of a word to get a special meaning across. Isn't this the pattern you use with these familiar remarks?

> What is the matter?
> How are you feeling?
> Is he angry?

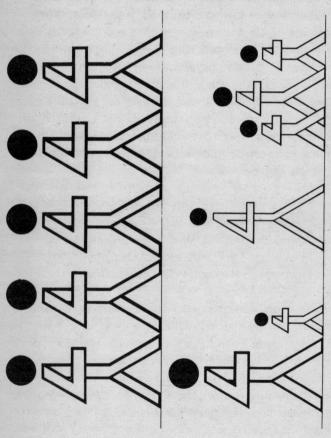

The stresses in French, Spanish, or Italian can be pictured like the pattern on the top, while English would look like the bottom row.

Even more difficult for the person learning our intonation pattern is that we sometimes shift our pitch by sliding down in the middle of a syllable. That really adds an ear-catching touch. It's like throwing a curved ball when all the others have been straight. Here a curved line shows where to bend your voice down.

The dinner is ⌐co⌐ld.
What time did you ⌐ca⌐ll?
I've waited all day ⌐lo⌐ng.
He hasn't said a ⌐wo⌐rd.

Another word for slide is inflection. Inflection added a stronger emotional coloring to the phrase above. Just one inflection can change the whole meaning of the sentence, even without a change in emotional tone. For example, if you wanted to say that you saw a black bird instead of a brown one, you'd simply use this intonation pattern.

I saw a ⌐black ⌐bird.

But if you actually saw a specific species of bird, the blackbird, you'd use the slide.

I saw a ⌐black ⌐bird.

The slide or inflection is thought by linguists to be the most beautiful and important characteristic of speech. Without it, speech is deadly monotonous. You'll see how automatically it is used in some more examples, and then you can begin to expand its use to other words. Slide down these words and become aware of some more inflections you probably already use.

It's time for class to ⌐e⌐nd.
What are ⌐you⌐ doing ⌐h⌐ere?
I don't think ⌐that⌐ is a good ⌐id⌐ea.
When do you ⌐pl⌐an to leave?

The above exercises involve the process of de-automatization. In order to help you learn to use slides consciously, I've given visual cues with the lines and encouraged you to listen to your voice make pitch adjustments to enhance meaning. Drawing the lines yourself will help more. A curve in the vertical line indicates a slide in the word. In addition to the marks used so far, separate different thoughts with two diagonal lines and then after glancing at the sentence, look up and say it.

I can tell you ⌐ th⌐is://it can't be done.
I don't want to go;//it's too ⌐ri⌐sky.
I say he can; he says he can't.
I think I know. But I won't tell.
If you want me to, I'll call her.
What do you want with a car? The bus is quicker!
You can do it in writing or orally.

If you're a fast visual learner, you're probably already well into the process of de-automatizing your monotonous vocal patterns after these few exercises. Many people aren't and it will take a period of marking and reading some of the most-used phrases to teach their voices to slide. After a week of practice, one student said he began to imagine peoples' conversations marked for intonation in print over their heads.

It's amazing what the mind can devise to help learn something new. After that student was able to vary his own intonation easily, the "intonational printing" disappeared. From that incident, I developed the technique of suggesting that students try picturing in their minds how particularly interesting phrases would look when marked for intonation. Here are some for you to try to picture:

> Get out and don't come back.
> I'll love you forever, no matter what!
> I'm tired of the same old line.

Another part of the de-automatization process is telling the body to put some interest into the voice. You are working toward vocal melody. Pitch, of course, is your main tool. As you say the word "melody," you can hear your voice change pitch to produce the different sounds in the word. Its natural elusive transitions resulted in its selection as one of the five most beautiful words in the English language. With enthusiastic agreement, I selected it as the name for my daughter and altered the spelling to personalize it for her. The musical quality inherent in words like melody can be a natural characteristic in a voice.

Some speech authorities identify pitch as the single most important feature of a distinctive voice. Psychologists have said it is an index of inner feelings. Suppose your friend John tells you he is dying of a rare disease.

Automatically, you will select a lower key than usual to reply, and probably your words will lengthen with slides that show sympathy. John senses that you deeply care about him from the melody pattern of your voice. On the other hand, some people show absolutely no emotional response in their voices no matter what you say. Perhaps you find yourself exaggerating even minor problems in hope that you'll motivate more feeling. You exaggerate by using more vocal melody.

Results of studies of vocal melody and emotion show that joy, happiness, and good news use a higher key; sadness, sorrow, and bad news, a lower. There is also much more variety in children than adults. This is probably true because children feel freer in expressing emotion. Often the signs of the control are written on the faces of adults in the taletelling lines, which point out the muscles that try to obey emotional restrictions. Many voices become dull, monotonous, and inflexible simply because they haven't been used creatively for years. I can usually predict the approximate age of an adult on the telephone by melody content. The surest way I know to sound younger, if you want to (many people don't), is to put melody back into your voice. When you hear your voice going up and down easily, you'll begin to feel younger, too.

Even though you may be among the many who have developed the habit of using very few voice changes, you can, within a very short time, completely change this habit. Start where you are. That simple advice was brought home to me when a handicapped woman with no speech came for help. First I taught her to put her lips together and say, "mmmm." Using strange-smelling paint supplies and toiletries, I taught her intonation patterns of "mmmm" for "good" and "bad."

Mmmm ⌐ mmmm
Mmmm _ mmmm

Studies show that smelling produces the strongest and most readily recalled memories. Situations surrounding toileting and eating also produce strong learning. In the bathroom, I taught her to indicate with her "mmmm," yes or no.

Mmmmm
Mmmm _ Mmmmmm!

Using pictures of fat men, short men, handsome men, mean-looking men, old men, young men, elegantly dressed men, poorly dressed men, and just plain guys, I taught her to slide to indicate her preferences. What a variety of inflection I heard. I added changes in my posture and gestures to help her understand the variety of responses possible for shades of meaning. Here are the two basic patterns. After you're tried these, think of each one of your friends and react with a different "mmm" variation for each one. Experiment with drawing out or reducing the length of the sounds, too.

Mmmmmmmmmmmm mmmmmmmmmm!
Mmm!

The noncommittal "mmm, mmm" that psychologists of the nondirective school are reputed to use is the most difficult to teach. If you aren't careful, that "mmm,

mmm" sounds like you agree with whatever is being said. You may have heard the story of the reflective psychologist who stuck to his training and responded with "mmm, mmm" regardless of what the patient said. The patient shouted, "I'm going to jump out of the window!" The inept psychologist responded with what he thought was another noncommittal "mmm, mmm" and when he looked up the patient was gone — out the window! Here's the pattern the man interpreted as agreement to his proposed leap.

Mmm mmm

Perhaps there really is no noncommital sound. Each person may interpret one to mean what he or she feels it should mean, or what he or she needs it to mean at some particular moment. Therefore, voice melody, the chosen key, the inflectional slides, and the up and down intonation patterns can expand the meaning of one sound to ten or more different things. Try using "oh" or "oh, oh" to communicate these reactions. Read the sentence silently, then say "oh" or "oh, oh" aloud to communicate the meaning of the complete thought. Don't forget the slide.

That's hard to believe. That's really puzzling. I understand perfectly. I dropped it. That's great! That's terrible! What did you say? You're so loving. You're disgusting. I'm aching all over. I'm very tired.

You can do the same thing with "ah." Practice as you read this tale.

A beautiful damsel (ah) fell in love with a brave and handsome (ah) employee of the U.S. Government (ah). It was during the war years (ah) and her father beseeched her not to marry him (ah). The young man (ah) insisted upon immediate nuptials (ah). However, just before the wedding was to take place (ah), a jealous former lover appeared (ah). He warned the bridegroom not to marry the beautiful young women (ah), because serious charges were about to be brought against her father (ah). The young woman fainted (ah). The father was furious (ah) and demanded to know what the charges were. The jealous young man (ah) pointed his finger at the father and said, "You are a spy in the U.S. Mint!" (ah).

Then the bridegroom collapsed, groaning, "Oh my God, her father's a mint spy!"

The father shrank back and said, "You know I'm a spy in the mint!"

If you ran those last two words together, you're going to say

"Ahhhh ⎡hhh."

If you had careful control of your emphasis techniques, you did not call her father a mince pie. Stressing the wrong syllable can create all kinds of verbal trouble. As you've already practiced stressing words by raising the pitch, you're now primed for the next stress technique, intensity. If you can remember back to grade school when you learned to read, you

147

know you probably hit every syllable with the same amount of force much like a typist striking all the keys with equal pressure. "Oh, look. See Spot. See Spot run. Look, look, look." Indeed, I would say that this is the best example of using intensity *not* to convey meaning. Unfortunately, some people never learn to read differently as they grow older. Frequent examples of this occurred on the old television series, "This is Your Life." Former friends of the person whose story was being told were brought in to tell their part in his or her life. Very often these people's reactions were spoken in a flat, monotonous style as they read from a television cue card. They did not realize how embarrassingly insincere they sounded because of their failure to use intensity and pitch changes. In the chapter on loudness I said that intensity was the easiest way to bring interest into speech. All that is needed is emphasis on the words that are significant. If you remember those fifty most-used words, you might have noticed that many of them were unstressed "function" words — articles (a, an, the), prepositions (to, of, in), personal pronouns (I, me, he, him, it), possessive adjectives (my, his, your), relative pronouns (who, that, which), common conjunctions (and, but, that, as, if), and verbs (be, have, do, will, would, shall, should, can, could, may, might, must). You may be able to think of times when you stressed these words appropriately. However, as you learn to express more feeling through words, those words you stress will change, and you'll get your message across.

Your message will be expressed in words with content, not the little function words. Content words are nouns, verbs (except those above), adjectives, adverbs, demonstratives (this, that, these, those), and interrogatives (who, when, why). Once you begin thinking about content words in what you say, your voice will cooperate in selecting the right touch of intensity in the places that will build meaning. Calling your attention to content words, something you probably haven't thought about for a long time, will help to de-automatize present habits. Start listening for content words in the conversation of your friends, and even though their speech may flow so evenly you are scarcely aware of the words they are stressing, you'll begin to absorb their meaning. You'll recognize subtle changes in intensity on certain words that reveal carefully covered emotions.

To begin to feel your present use of intensity, no matter how slight it may be, underline the words you want to emphasize in these sentences.

I can't go out tonight because I'm too tired.
I wish I knew where I could borrow some money.
His wife doesn't know anything about it.
Beneath every cold voice is a warm body.
My voice is the cutting edge of my personality.

The usual pattern in English, which you observed as you marked the sentence, is a stressed word followed by unstressed words in an irregular pattern. The amount of stress and the intervals between the emphasized words vary.

French, Spanish, Italian, and many other languages are mechanically regular with series of bursts of sound all about the same length and force. Teachers of these languages tell struggling students that the even accent pattern is much easier to use than that of English. If we used that type of intensity, we might be signed up as a comedy act! We have a great variety of stressed and unstressed words, some big stresses, some little ones. Some are created by raising pitch, others with just intensity, some with loudness, others by lengthening sounds.

Many people do not reflect their individuality in their habits of stressing words. Patterns of word stress need not be an inescapable steel trap if a little time is devoted to practice. Begin with the following familiar comments and underline, bracket, and circle the words you would emphasize for three different interpretations: underline words to represent interpretation A, bracket words for B, and circle words for C. Of course, assign emphasis based on the meaning of the complete sentence. Then look up from the page and say the sentence as spontaneously as possible. I've marked the first one as an example.

If it should <u>rain</u>, [we'll] call off the (whole) (thing.)
I don't know what I'm going to do, but I've got to do something.
There are two ways to do it and we'll do it one way or another.
My reactions to you are good, bad, and indifferent; that proves you're human.
A dinner without candles and cloth napkins spoils his appetite. He's a restaurant snob.
I'm sorry you waited so long. My car broke down.
Put yourself in his place. He had little choice.
There's no time to lose, we've got to do it now.
Under great pressure, he always caves in!
Put your heart in your work and you'll enjoy your life

more.
Put your foot in your mouth and you won't!

You may notice that your intensity pattern was balanced by pauses. Sound balanced by silence gives meaning to what is said. Spine-chilling suspense stories are dependent upon the use of silence to heighten the anticipation of the worst. Pauses are quiet punctuation marks. The writer has commas, periods, question and exclamation marks, dots, and dashes. We follow them automatically as we read. Yet few of us are able to use the pause when speaking. Again, we've become so programmed to be fast, frequent, and fluent, that we're totally unaware of our lack of pauses. "It's the pause that refreshes," a commercial reminds us. Try now to bring some refreshing pauses into your conversations by working with these examples. For a short pause, mark one line; for a medium one, two lines; and for a really poignant pause, three lines. You can decide on the amount of time given each pause. The examples show a few typical pause patterns I use. You mark the remaining sentences.

/If you're in a hurry,/don't wait for me./
/Now listen to me:///You'll stay home, or take the consequence./
/Are you guessing,///or do you really know?/
/This is one type of pasta//and this is another./
/Buy it quick./That's a bargain!/
I don't know. You tell me.
I'll bet I've tried that a dozen times. It never works.
Light the fuse, and then run.
If you phrase correctly, you'll never run out of breath.

If you mean what you say, say what you mean.

I lifted the lid and out jumped a frog!

You have every right to your opinions, but I don't agree with them.

I wish I could tell you how much I care, but I can't find the words.

Your respect means more to me than all the money in the world.

Please don't let me down, I've counted on your going with me.

That doesn't surprise me one bit; that's the way she always acts.

Pauses are part of voice power. The greatest speakers ever known were masters of the pause. In other words, they didn't let their mouths get ahead of their brains. A spoken phrase is a series of words bounded by pauses. It does not need to coincide with grammatical phrases, clauses, or sentences, and it may not coincide with punctuation marks. It need only enhance meaning and it better not detract from it. If you are to read anything before an audience, the best help you can give yourself is to mark your manuscript into meaningful phrases. But be careful. The phrases must fit your breathing schedule, or you may interrupt a phrase with a gasp. The professional singer always plans breaths to give the one energy in the right places. You can improve anything you read before an audience by putting a red dot in the places you will breathe. You need one breath with every six or seven words. This means two or three breaths every ten seconds of speaking. That may sound like a lot of breathing; the only way to know for sure is to test yourself before facing your audience, and then give yourself some leg room. If you let the red dots help keep your breathing on target for at least a paragraph or two, your stage fright will probably exit before you do.

Tightening up muscles, forgetting to breathe regularly as you speak or read, and standing glued to one spot will destroy the most carefully constructed introduction. The audience will remember only your nervousness, not your message. If you want to get rid of nervousness before an audience, *practice being nervous*. Stand in front of a mirror, full length if possible, and do your complete nervous routine. Everyone has his own variation on this theme. Some breathe with short sighs and wring their hands. Others sway back and forth. Still others stiffen their legs, lick their lips, wipe imaginary perspiration off their brows, and swallow repeatedly. Flicking imaginary lint, smoothing your hair, rubbing your nose, giving your arm a quick scratch, shifting your shoulders, stretching your chin up as though your collar were too tight, clearing your throat, hitching up your pants or skirt, taking a quick look down to make sure everything is straight, tucked, and zipped, and grabbing a quick knuckle-nibble are all part of the nervous act you can practice till you do each with finesse. This negative practice will train you out of every temptation to be caught in the nervousness trap. No longer will these habits remain hidden from you, but not from your audience.

Scrap the myths that an audience loves a nervous speaker, that they don't respond to a smooth speaker, and that somehow ineptness endears one to professionals. You can stop making excuses for nervousness and stop devouring the phony reassurance others will feed you when you've done your nervous worst.

Self-talk can solidify the self-confident sound, as well as

rid you of nervous mannerisms. Self-talk is best done before a mirror, too, but if that is really uncomfortable at first, take an assignment that's easy for you without a mirror. Suppose your problem is a rapid speaking rate. Write on a card. "To slow my rate, I will talk as rapidly as I can about my job for three minutes every day for one week." You might need to make some notes about the points you will talk about, or you may find that you quickly run out of material when you're speaking at the typical fast rate of 180 to 210 words per minute. My students like to choose the topics that typically trigger their fastest speech. For some, that is discrimination in some form; for others, the evils of a big federal government; and for still others, it is politics and religion. It's amazing how well this technique works to help put the brakes on your tongue. Every time you hear someone else going a mile a minute, you'll mentally change gears into a slower rate for yourself. With this new set, you will be able to use expressive intonation and emphasis that were not possible at a rapid rate.

There is no other technique I know that will move you toward increasing expressive intonation and emphasis than the practice of self-talk. You become your own feedback system. You hear, feel, see, and maybe even taste the words. You become unified in thought, feeling, and action. When you get everything all going in one direction, you impress strongly upon your mind your strength of will and purpose. What is more convincing than *you yourself,* demonstrating that you can discipline yourself to practice? You're now ready to put the finishing touch on your voice power trademark. With clear pronunciation and effective diction, you will make the final transformation towards voice power.

NINE

Your Trademarks: Pronunciation and Diction

We each have a bold, legible trademark that suggests to others our individuality. If we were to list the elements of this trademark in the order of what a listener reacts to first, pronunciation and diction might head the list. Pronunciation can indicate the region where we grew up and subliminally suggest our attachment to the attitudes popular there. Diction and choice of words quickly identify level of education, personal tastes, and the warmth or coldness of our temperament. Pronunciation and diction outline our personal styles.

Although we rarely analyze the meaning of style, we intuitively understand the expression "Do they have style!" Style is more than clothing, money, posture, personality, position, and beauty. It encompasses the depth and breadth of all aspects of character and personality. When one famous orator wrote "Style *is* the man," he was not simply restating the familiar German saying *Kleider machen Leute* (clothes make people). He was saying that style is created by cultural background, education, economic background, body carriage, health, and individual creativity. Their interaction produces our outlooks on life, attitudes, purposes, beliefs, abilities, and temperaments.

Many people are discouraged to learn their style and personal trademark began at a very early age when they had little choice in the matter. Sudden realization may come when they view themselves on a videotape and see that their mannerisms no longer reflect their accomplishments or inner person. A similar shock often comes when people participate in a television game show that is aired at a later date. Viewing themselves in their own living rooms, they may be mortified to see that they appear to be fictional characters with speech styles and spontaneous gestures that obviously identify their shortcomings. One woman I know was motivated to discover that she had the problem of the cockney flower girl in *Pygmalion*. Although she had graduated from an elite women's college, she had retained a regional flavor in her speech that was distracting and gave the impression of little education. Like the approach used by Professor Henry Higgins with the cockney Eliza Doolittle, patience, determination, and daily practice on the specific errors in pronunciation and intonation improved her style.

Like this woman, you probably are not aware of the choices you have made that loudly proclaim your style. Can you find a word to describe it? Simple was the word used to describe Will Rogers's style. Brilliant has been used to describe John Kennedy, florid for Barry Goldwater, plain for Jimmy Carter, intellectual for Adlai Stevenson, cultivated for Jacqueline Onassis, dull for Calvin Coolidge, and straightforward for Ralph Nader. Are you a straight-down-the-line feminist, a rabble-rousing red-neck, a mild-mannered professor, a dyed-in-the-wool Democrat? Do you know how others describe you? Sometimes that's a clue to the style you have of which you're totally unaware. You may have a trademark that you want to trade in.

Take a few minutes to answer a few of these questions, and then see if you can come up with some words to describe your style.

What are your favorite phrases?
What slang words do you use?
What new words have challenged you lately?
Do you think this universe is a friendly place?
What is your main goal in life?
How much education is absolutely essential for successful independent living?
What is your attitude about prosperity?
What abilities do you have that you use?
What is your main interest?
What words best describe your temperament with people *not* in your family?
Do you have a strong regional flavor to your life (speech, dress, religion, politics, or work)?
Do you belong to several different groups and regularly attend meetings? Are you an action-oriented person or a reactor?

From the above answers, fill in this sentence description of your style.

I am a _____ (temperament) person with a _____ (limited, unrestricted, unexpanding, expanding) life-style who believes the universe is basically _____ (indifferent, friendly, unfriendly), that prosperity is _____ (easy, difficult) to develop, that my life is _____ (easy, difficult) to develop, that my life is _____ (unfulfilled, partially fulfilled, being fulfilled) through my _____ (purposes, beliefs, abilities, interests), and that I can do _____ (nothing, little, much) about _____ (none, some, most) of the circumstances, conditions, and people in my life and affairs. My style is _____ (distinct, indistinct) from others close to me. My friends would probably describe it as _____ . I can honestly say I'd call it _____ . My pronunciation and choice of words (accurately, inaccurately) fit the style I want for myself.

Your language style is made up of grammar, pronunciation, diction, and vocabulary. Most of us want a language style that expresses our individuality and enables us to communicate with others. Successful people take full responsibility for communicating information accurately, completely, and with good will, regardless of the age or background of the listener. Understanding, friendliness, sincerity, simplicity, and familiar and relaxed language result in a disarming, natural speech style.

Good style does include correct grammar. Although English is a living language that is continuously expanding and changing, the standard at any time is based on the common sense of many people. An example of the best usage of our time is the writing in large daily newspapers. It's straightforward, uses correct English constructions, and encompasses various personal styles from the bantering Buchwald to the intellectually stimulating Sevareid. English need not mean stuffiness.

One thing correct grammar does mean is careful use of vocabulary. In a newspaper article, slang is reserved for making specific, colorful points. Slang-filled speech full of four-letter obscenities and "right-ons" lacks creativity. The problem goes beyond slang to rigid vocabularies. Not only is slang overused by Americans — from young people to middle-aged people trying to come across as young people — but other words are drawn only from narrow vocabularies. Several hundred thousand words are available but the average person uses only a few hundred. Many of these express little meaning or are used incorrectly. When people seek education or medical care, they ask, "Why not the best?" This philosophy is appropriate for grammar and word choice, too. English can be very elegant.

However, Americans have a hysterical fear of affectation. False elegance is felt to be un-American and we all shout hurrah for the art of plain talk. But it is important to remember that *all* speech is acquired. The only affectation is in parading insincerely a mastery you don't have or knowledge you don't possess, and in that case you're likely to be a target regardless of your dignified diction.

In our country, formal English is rarely heard. Using phrases such as "whom do you mean?" and "I felt badly" can set you apart, maybe even result in mimicry. Professor Higgins would emphatically agree that you create a new person if you elevate speech and language. But you also create new problems if you rise too high or fall too low. What's *too* low?

"See'n as how you gals and gents tossed in a buck to get pass the gate, I'm gonna give you the lowdown on the folks that use ta hang their hats here. First off, I ain't gonna mince no words, 'cuz I'm tellin' it like it was." Before he begins his next sentence, you have already made some unconscious decisions about his level of education and ability to use language, and the amount of confidence you will give his information. His diction is substandard because it contains too much slang, provincialisms, and colloquial style. Yet it can be argued that his style suggests rich tradition and the strength of the soil. When regional language is natural to the speaker, curbing it can lead to a lack of spontaneity and force. Regional usages developed when people lived in small areas and were socially isolated. Without the flow of people and ideas, language develops its own peculiarities within a certain area. Southern drawls, Appalachian variations on the drawl, Brooklynese, the Boston *r*, and the midwestern twang originated before television, radio, trains, cars, planes, and telephones. Given two hundred years more, they probably will have their exit, and we'll have amalgamated American.

Today, new slang expressions develop from many diverse interest groups. That same old principle carries on; groups in isolation develop their own language that few others will understand except for two or three of the most common words. Slang doesn't just come from the racetrack, the carnival, and the racketeers. It breeds as easily among baseball fans, airplane enthusiasts, steelworkers, hot-rodders, soldiers, sailors, ham radio operators, teenagers, and jazz fans.

Out of an average vocabulary of ten to twenty

thousand words, 10 percent is slang. Linguists say that most slang develops from the male population who create a hefty number of expressions to avoid sounding feminine. Another source is food. When people are drunk, we say they are pickled, fried, or boiled, and with the dawn of the popularity of violence, bombed, stoned, plastered, or smashed. She's some cookie, or a real tomato have been replaced with other images that are not as predominately sexual as you might guess. Only a small percentage of slang is sexual, and with the new freedom of women, many of the favorite male terms have invaded their vocabularies. I also notice that women like to describe the worst in men with labels from the animal kingdom. Frogs, turkeys, snakes, squirrels, louses, octopuses, and worms are some of the uncomplimentary references.

The dictionary writers cannot begin to record all of the new slang of frustration between the sexes, which is just as well. I am convinced that for every slang word we use well, there are ninety-nine slang words that it would be better not to use at all. Unless part of your trademark is to let people know what subgroups you belong to, you will want to begin to eliminate most of the slang and some of the overworked, worn-out expressions. If you want an individualistic sound, you can't parrot your peers. Here's a list a student of mine decided to find fresh words for:

neat	boo-booed
jerk	make out
goldfish	cost an arm
feed my face	and a leg

up the creek	groovy
make a score	fruitcake
far out	kill time
goof off	pull a boner
gone bananas	rip-off

An older student who frequently spoke publicly had these phrases on his discard list:

the inner man	in a few well-chosen words
conspicuous by his absence	the dawn of a new day
all or nearly all	methods in his madness
too funny for words	trials and tribulations
in our midst	mockery of justice
last but not least	this fair land
at the parting of the ways	fine-feathered friends
only too glad	with bated breath
interesting and instructive	a long-felt want
the logical moment	along these lines
through his untiring efforts	so quiet you could have heard a pin drop
without further ado	
needs no introduction	meaningful experience

Do you find the following list of expressions that have been around a long time are an integral part of your speech? You won't find them in newspapers or magazines, nor will you often hear them on television or radio. They are perpetuated by people speaking automatically from the mass reservoir of quick, thoughtless communication.

the blind leading the blind

far be it for me

hard as a rock

straight as an arrow

thick as fog

stubborn as a mule

in the nick of time

clear as crystal

heavy as lead

heart of gold

sturdy as an oak

quiet as a mouse

easy as pie

works like a horse

cuts like butter

dumb as a doorbell

waddles like a duck

black as the ace of spades

horse of a different color

smart as a whip

dumb bunny

thick as mud

peaches and cream
   complexion

ugly as sin

tight as a drum

dead as a doornail

cute as a button

sings like a canary

a rule of thumb

sings like an angel

jealous as a cat

water under the bridge

dog tired

quick as a wink

smokes like a chimney

drinks like a fish

quick as a flash

slick as a whistle

crooked as a Philadelphia
   lawyer

eyes like a hawk

loose as a goose

limp as a dish rag

high as a kite

voice like a frog

wicked as a witch

happy as a lark

sour as a grape

strong as a moose

bright as a penny

blue as the ocean

sober as a judge

fast as a bullet

runs likes a fox

gift of gab

struts like a peacock

red as a beet

sweet as sugar candy

penny wise and pound foolish

read him like a book

haven't seen hide nor hair of
   them

sweep it under the rug

green as grass

drunk as a skunk

don't cross your bridges, etc.

fluffy as a pillow

sleeps like a baby

in a pig's eye

called on the carpet

fresh as a daisy

meaner than a mule

cute as a bug

under the table deal

good as gold

You probably can add at least five more that I didn't record during my month's listening to conversations. There is no doubt that they add color and fun to conversations. But for a fresh trademark, you don't want antique similies. To begin personalizing your language, pick out the ones on the list that you have used in the past month and deliberately find a fresh comparison. Write down three on a card and the people or situations you will use them with. Here's one student's sample.

Expression	Change	To whom	When
Fresh as a daisy	Fresh as rain in the pines. ("You look fresh as the rain in the pines.")	Wife	When I come home.
Don't cross your bridges, etc.	Don't go out in tomorrow's rain, when it's not raining today!	Secretary	When she begins to worry, "What if."
Happy as a lark	Happy as a baby in a jumper	Associates	To describe the satisfaction of a new client

164

Not knowing where to start can often prevent reaching the finish line. Here are some easy starters to help your mind start finding fresh words. It may take a week before you see or think of just the right word or phrase to give a new flavor to these old standbys.

sleeps like a _____	works like a _____
eats like a _____	talks like a _____
drinks like a _____	runs like a _____
walks like a _____	sees like a _____

Improving word usage can be fun if you include friends in your vigilance against worn-out phrases. Pointing out overworked expressions to one another can become a game and increases our awareness of our responsibility to enhance the best in our culture and discourage the worst.

Recently in a midwestern university, one faculty group decided to call attention to badly used words. Each week they would selected an overworked modern word. Anyone caught using the word donated a quarter to the library fund. The news media picked up the story and the whole country joined in the word-watcher game.

Recently, Audrey Wallace, a weary-word watcher from Orange, California, wrote me that "interesting" had become the adjective of the careful intellectual. Not wishing to give a judgment of good or bad, you could always describe anything as interesting, and be considered acceptably responsive. Sometimes it is substituted for "amusing," when actually it means entertaining, diverting, or fascinating. It is often used in place of "unusual" when curious, exceptional, unique, original, extraordinary, remarkable, fantastic, bizarre, exotic, unfamiliar, or unconventional would be more accurate. An "interesting" person might be well-informed, whimsical, picturesque, quick-witted, artistic, enthralling, verbose, scintillating, dynamic, or outright roguish. A multitude of books are merely described as interesting instead of stimulating, informative, enlightening, absorbing, shocking, or penetrating. And speakers are often similarly classified instead of being called instructive, enthusiastic, challenging, morbid, engrossing, illuminating, encouraging, imaginative, prejudiced, or judgmental. In addition to overusing the word, many also mispronounce it by omitting the "t" or by failing to accent the first syllable.

A frequent argument for not using words that don't appear frequently in daily usage is that they may not be understood. But there are many simple, plain words familiar to all that can diversify speech. You can show off greater verbal facility when the meaning need not be instantaneously understood, as with the written word. Here is a list of both plain and fancy words that can enhance your vocabulary and can be used at your discretion.

Plain	Fancy	Plain	Fancy
drink	imbibe	improve	ameliorate
read	peruse	pretty	attractive
begin	inaugurate	foul	repulsive
say	remark	funny	mischievous
help	assist	rotten	decomposed
secretly	surreptitiously	plump	rotund
enough	sufficient	round	circular
buy	purchase	basics	rudiments

166

end	terminate	rue	regret
breach	infringement	building	edifice
rules	regulations	face	visage
nice	amiable	hasten	expedite
good	delicious	try	endeavor
awful	calamitous	foe	antagonist
base	contemptible	gifts	donations
go	proceed	give	provide
ask	inquire	slight	inconsequential
leg	limb	lie	prevaricate
home	domicile	sad	disconsolate
best	optimum	sale	transaction
start	commence	fat	corpulent
great	distinguished	stupid	unenlightened
fine	elegant	false	erroneous
scared	alarmed	do	execute
usual	accustomed	persist	persevere
friendly	amiable	puzzled	perplexed
rid	eliminate	odd	peculiar
walk	ambulate	widespread	prevalent
turn	rotate	repay	remunerate
rough	irregular	unhappy	despondent
hurt	injure	think	ruminate
rude	discourteous	wages	remuneration
carry out	perform	wise	sagacious
risky	perilous	member	constituent
ruinous	pernicious	disaster	calamity
offer	proposal	evade	equivocate
sorry	penitent	set up	establish

If your voice power trademark is going to include an enriched vocabulary, adjectives are a good way to start. Luxuriate when you are talking about a book, a sunset, or the person you love. In the discussion of "interesting," I shared with you some of my favorites. You'll find twenty-five more among my fancy word list, and if you open any novel, you will find many more. The editorial pages of the newspapers have a wealth of words that I'd like to use more often. Pungent, incredulity, transmogrifying, and smidgen are out of editorials I scanned this week.

If you really enjoy words, a friend of mine suggests trying the "root" method to expand vocabulary. He confided that by memorizing only thirteen roots, he covered 15,000 common words. His list of roots is delightfully easier to work with than the eight hundred primary elements the learned professors list in the etymological dictionaries.

capere: take, seize (concept, precept, capitulate)
ducere: lead (produce, deduce, reduce)
facere: make, do (sufficient, facility, faculty)
ferre: bear, carry (offer, transfer, refer)
graphein: write (monograph, graphic, telegraph)
legein: say, study of (dialogue, epilogue, logic)
mittere: send (remit, intermittent, commit)
plicare: fold (complicate, complicacy, uncomplicate)
ponere: put, place (indisposed, deposed, deposition)
scribere: write (transcribe, inscription, description)
specere: see (suspect, aspect, spectacles)
stare: stand (insistence, desist, resist)

tendere: stretch (extension, tendon, pretend)

The meaning of the common prefixes are listed below.

in: into, not	inter: between
un: not	ob: against
pre: before	mono: alone, one
de: away from	epi: upon
ad: to, towards	com: together with
ex: out of	re: back, again
pro: forward	dis: apart from
over: above	sub: under
mis: wrong	trans: across, beyond

You can buy a vocabulary development book and in three weeks have word power to match your voice power. *Word Power Made Easy*, Norman Lewis, Doubleday, has a three-week program and also has help with grammar, spelling, and pronunciation. *Programmed Vocabulary: Steps Toward Improved Word Power*, James I. Brown, Appleton-Century Crofts, is another helpful book. Both of these authors have written many books about words and have unique approaches to keep you expanding your word skills. Your public library should have them. Newer vocabulary helps include *Twelve Ways to Build a Vocabulary*, Archibald Hart, B & N Publishers; *How to Build a Better Vocabulary*, Maxwell Nurnberg and Morris Rosenblum, Popular Library; and Nancy Davis's *Vocabulary Improvement. A Program for Self-Instruction*, McGraw.

If you've chosen as part of your voice power trademark the use of a vocabulary to stamp you as a well-educated person, here are some words to help achieve that goal, according to one study.

altruism	immutable
idealism	perception
romanticism	conceptualization
alienated	anticipatory
valence	homeostasis
contiguous	random
quantitative	organism
quasi	illusory

You probably would not use the complete list even weekly, but you should find many of them appearing on a regular basis in your conversation. All that the study demonstrated was that these words were used by college-educated persons. Yet more important than knowing sixteen words used by the well-educated man is having at your command specific words that make your message come alive. You could say, "He closed the door and went home," but it might be more accurate and much more ear-catching if you say, "He slammed the door and ran home." Effective diction does not need to include many long complex words. Here are my favorite "brief words":

ail	iota	mite	sprite	foil
soothe	goad	pierce	coy	vague
clip	spur	lilt	tempt	sloth
lure	gnaw	trim	scorn	alluring
chafe	stroll	lusty	buff	sinewy
trial	beguile	ravish	craze	rouse
crave	dearth	gloss	virile	vaunt
pique	nettle	mirth	vex	odious
spurn	serene	sheer	wiry	haze
gaunt	qualm	risk	cull	ogle
verve	glorify	savory	smite	stanch
trifling	gall	burly	spume	ashen
austere	toggle	glowing	dire	cryptic
skew	furrow	puff	gasp	paltry
toady	dupe	souse	sear	fond
wither	shrivel	bully	rowdy	cynic
douse	dregs	quash	oaf	placid
stifle	tumult	saunter	laud	ream
mock	tipple	abhor	artful	grovel
hoax	suave	plod	cower	thrive
brisk	dainty	morose	taunt	abash
agile	robust	cite	quote	matchless
deny	tidbit	dash	joyous	irk
fret	zealous	imp	fiend	frolic
hurl	fling	fracas	shuffle	pester
quaint	modish	pang	awe	testy
crusty	coax	veer	raspy	realm

Most of my students are surprised to realize they
know and can pronounce every word in the list. Their
main problem is that they're caught in the habit-
vocabulary trap and don't think to use fresh words.

Training yourself to use more of what you *know* that is actually more specific and more colorful is a difficult task to undertake on your own, but it can be done. In a class situation, it's easy to break into couples, pick out ten words and a topic. Discussing films, radio, and TV is the easiest route for most. Sometimes sports, hobbies, and mutual interests form the background for discussions using these words. If you write personal letters, keep the list beside you and see how many words you can use to bolster impact. Remember, your old words are taped in your head and replay automatically unless they are taped over with better words. The new tape must be related to your own total communication situation, If you don't practice the specific kinds of situations you are frequently in, you'll revert to your frayed way of expression.

By now, you should be beginning to be very careful of pronunciation. Just by reading the words and thinking about change, you have made an important gain in voice power because you have been reprogramming your enunciation. You will not always have to be slow and careful, but you know you can't drive at normal speeds until all of the essentials of driving are almost automatic. Automatic is how pronunciation and diction should be before you attempt to speak more rapidly. For practice, try these tongue twisters *as rapidly as you can say them*. Then use a speed at which you make every sound perfectly. Notice your problem sounds and sort those out for continued practice. Showing off with "Peter Piper" won't do anything for your whistling, lisping, or mushy "s" sound. If you take a look in the mirror, you will see what the jaw, lips, and cheeks must do to support the movement of the tongue. Be careful that you don't get your eyebrows into the act!

(b) Rubber baby buggy bumpers.

(b) The big black bug bled big black blood.

(b) The baby buggy bulged badly barging between Bob and Barbara.

(b) Baby bear bruised his bare bottom by bumping boisterously before breakfast.

(g) Golly guesses gone goofy gum great geniuses gargantuously.

(g) Great gobs of green goosey goat guts glorify Gladys Gootspy.

(g) Greta grabbed Greg's grater and grated greater green grapes grievously.

(k) Can cotton candy coat clean cold combs?

(k) Karen cared candidly causing Calvin's cunning continued catastrophe.

(k) Kate kicked Cortney, clipped Curtis, and cut class quickly with Kelly.

(l) Lester likes lemons lovelier while Peter prefers peppers peeled perfectly.

(l) Little Lilly fell pell-mell down the looming hill last but not least.

(l) If you slyly stick a sturdy stock of stalwart liquor in your liquor locker, it is surely slick to stick a strong lock on your stock for some joker who is slicker is going to trick you of your liquor if you fail to lock your liquor with a lock on your locker.

(m) Mad Mark Mims muttered mindlessly as he manfully mutilated many melancholy manicured maiden monkeys' monstrous manacles.

(n) Now nosey newsmen nonsensically nibble noodles, nuts, and Nordic nostoc nearly nightly noiselessly, a nostrum, normally.

(p) Pretty Polly, Patty's pal, typed a heap of papers promptly.

(p) If Peter Piper picked a peck of pickled peppers, how many pickled peppers did Peter Pipe pick? Probably, Penny pinching Peter paled piteously preventing poignant pepper picking presently.

(p) Please pass the peas, porridge, and potatoes promptly to petty Peppermint Patty, permitting perpetuating perkiness.

(r) Rarely Roger reads romantic recreation literature; really he prefers realistic regional redhots reflecting the ramblings of rogues.

(r) Right responses really result when recriminating ruthless rascals radically rearm rioters rashly rebelling.

(r) Rosalie ripped her red rambling roses rather rapidly from the front of her redwood ramshackle retreat.

(s) Susie sells sea shells down by the seashore, simultaneously sightseeing.

(s) The sinking steamer sunk suddenly spoiling Sam's snorkel sporting.

(s) Still soup savors silently, says serious Sally sullenly salting some salami.

(s) The sixth sheik's sixth sheep's sick.

(sh) She shells sea shells to shoddy shippers shirking at the seashore.

(sh) Shortsighted shirtless Shakespearean sheriffs shouted shrilly, "Sherry and shortcake."

(sh) Shameless Shannon shook the shepherd's shingled shelter shocking sheepish Shawnees by her shenanigans.

(sh) Plush cushions with short sashes were the chic fashion, she shuddered shyly.

(st, Tess missed the geese and the loose stymied rooster.

sk, The pest's nests on the masts and posts were destroyed by the gusts.

sts) The skunk sat on a stump; the skunk thought the stump stunk, but the stump thought the skunk stunk.

(t, d) Tins tied together tightly tipped the trailer; dazed, Don was ditched and dragged drearily dextrally. Tillie's knitted mitten fitted Tommy's tiny tumbling kitten.

(thd) He writhed about, breathed heavily, and mouthed his melodic melodies.

(w) The weary weepy women wept over the war waifs and weakened widows.

(wh) Where and why were you whispering and whimpering, my wheezing whippernapper?

(zh) On that occasion, the allusion to his decision caused derision.

(zh) The fission caused the usual explosion on the measure about the intrusion of the Persian division and the seizure of the treasure.

Often the tongue twisters do more of a service than just increasing flexibility and coordination. They shout loudly which sounds are still problematic.

Problems of lisping can still be corrected, even with adults. Even those lispers who feel they have to come to terms with their lisp are still better off without it. In many adult lispers, I have seen a characteristic swallowing pattern. They push their tongues against their upper teeth and gum ridge or between the teeth each time they swallow. Since swallowing occurs a couple of thousand times a day as we eat, drink, and take care of the constant flow of saliva, tongue action is unconscious and automatic. During speech, the tongue continues the thrusting used consistently in swallowing. The result can be a lisp or just a visibly flourishing tongue tip during talking.

Some orthodontists use a tongue rake or tongue catcher, a crib, or prongs to discourage the tongue thrust. The tongue quickly learns not to "risk the rake" and develops new positioning during swallowing.

Another solution is to enlist the help of an oral myofunctional therapist, a teacher, or speech specialist who specializes in tongue retraining. Many approaches are used for the clients, who frequently are children preparing for orthodontic treatment. Children do need the very best professional help obtainable to guide them through this problem. Some orthodontists believe the success of their orthodontic treatment depends upon it; others prefer the tongue devices. If the tongue is not trained to stop thrusting one way or another, it will push the teeth out again after the braces are removed.

As an adult with a tongue thrust problem, you probably are not in any orthodontic program, your teeth contour is stable, and you have the self-discipline, motivation, and emotional maturity to make some corrective efforts yourself. Even though you may not persist enough to change your swallowing pattern, the increased flexibility, strength, range of motion, and coordination that will result from your efforts will give better control of tongue, lips, jaw, and soft-palate for all speech sounds. Adult lispers tell me it's worse when they're tired or have been drinking. It makes good sense that conditioning these muscles would lessen the effects of fatigue and alcohol, which often do affect the crispness of speech, with or without a speech problem. Here's a list of activities for adult tongue thrusters.

1. Before a mirror, clench your front teeth, keeping lips apart, and say "sss" for twenty seconds.
2. Put your index finger behind your two biggest front teeth, touching the gum ridge. Push on the ridge firmly ten times.
3. Put your tongue tip on the same spot and push ten times. (Keep your mouth open.)
4. Clench your front teeth again, press the spot again with your tongue tip twenty times.
5. Click your tongue against that spot on the gum ridge ten times.
6. Take a sip of water, suck so that your cheeks come in, swallow.
7. If you have trouble, put your finger back on the gum ridge, suck, swallow.

8. Take a small sip of water, put your tongue on the gum ridge, suck, swallow. If your tongue slips down on your teeth or between them, you will be blowing, not sucking. (That's a tongue thrust.)

9. Whenever you drink, practice your correct swallow.

10. Place a small amount of peanut butter on gum ridge, practice the suck-swallow routine.

11. Practice saying, "cha, choo," with your tongue in the correct position on the gum ridge.

12. Practice licking your upper gum ridge with your tongue keeping your lips closed and your teeth together.

13. Practice strong tongue clicks raising as much of your tongue blade as possible.

14. Practice yawning and then swallow. Feel the activity in the back of the throat? With a tongue thrust, too many muscles overwork in the front of your face and mouth. Put your fingers on your Adam's apple as you yawn and swallow.

15. Increase back throat muscle activity. Open your mouth wide before a mirror so you can see your uvula, that hanging tiny finger-like piece of muscle. Pant vigorously so that it moves back and forth.

16. With tongue tip continuously pressing against the gum ridge of your upper front teeth, say, "hig, hag, hug, hog, huck," for two minutes.

17. Gargling also helps strengthen the muscles in the back of the throat and again pulls the tongue down and backward. Gargle every day.

18. Now check yourself before a mirror. Put your fingers lightly on your lips and swallow. There should be no lip movement or facial movement during the swallow. If you're still feeling lip movements and facial movements, you need more practice of everything so far. Those with the tongue-thrust-type swallow will have lines from the corners of their nose to their jaw, marking the muscle activity. If you do a "forced" swallow while putting your lips tightly together, you'll see the lines, even if you aren't a tongue thruster. Before long, you'll become so aware of all of the facial movements that accompany tongue thrusting that you'll spot it anywhere.

19. If you have an open bite, and your lips don't meet, a little stretching exercise will help. With a short upper lip, you probably find you can't swallow without using it. Try this. Put your index finger on your chin and thumb under your chin. Pull down. Bring your upper lip down to touch the lower lip and then relax. Thirty times before and after each meal will lengthen and strengthen the upper lip and help you move toward normal lip closure.

20. Buy a Waterpik and after you've cleaned your teeth, practice some rapid swallowing of the water spurting out. Use it to lightly rake down the tongue to stimulate that muscle. I also guide it under the tongue and all around the inside of the mouth to condition muscles of many of my clients. I alternate from light to strong streams and always stop before irritation starts. (Usually about three to five minutes is adequate.)

179

William Zickefoose, the founder of the International Association of Oral Myology, who has been retraining tongues for twenty years, says that he has success in 75 to 80 percent of his clients. The failures are those who fail to practice the techniques taught them. He stresses practicing before going to sleep to help the tongue continue the pattern all night. He makes practice tapes for his clients. If you're among those that don't succeed, you will still be well on your way to lisping less. Here are some exercises to accompany a tongue thrust program to help you shed your lisp at the same time.

1. Suck air in with your teeth together. Place your tongue on the spot on your gum ridge and with teeth lightly touching, say "sss" until you run out of breath.
2. Suck in air and let it out as you say each of these words. Be sure your tongue is on the gum ridge behind the upper two front teeth.

sin	still	seep	said
sad	sun	say	Sue
Sam	sag	sell	salt
seen	some	saw	sip
sale	so	Sal	sit

3. Now practice this list with the "s" on the end. The "t" before the "s" will help you keep your tongue in the right position.

eats	dots	mites
bites	boats	beets

cots	lights	sets
frights	pats	rights
cats	dotes	hits
tights	heats	tots
bats	dates	kites

4. Using a "t" in the middle, followed by the "s," you can practice the correct "s" position in the middle of the word. Actually, I don't believe there is only one position for "s"; we all make it slightly different. However, if you want to *correct* a lisp, use the tongue position that you would use for the "t" sound (or tongue tip on the gum ridge, which I have taught you in the swallowing section). Think as you repeat these. Be fully aware of where the tongue touches for the "s."

Pittsburgh	batsman	draughtsman
Matson	Trotsky	cat's-eye
boatsman	itself	Ditson
hotsy-totsy	catsup	jetsam
whatsoever	Datson	Plattsburgh
Dotson	flotsam	footsore
Watson	catsman	Cotson
Litson	Matsy	cat's-foot

5. You can continue a guaranteed perfect "s" by saying these two-word combinations, and again, keep your tongue tip high before you slide into the "s."

wet streets	light sandal	great sound
what city	hat store	sit still
net slipped	fat sparrow	let's see

181

hot soup	fight sanely	heat some
not so	might slip	might sip
wet sand	light ski	light snow
light satin	let's say	fat cigar
what saddle	hot sandwich	neat system
wet soap	might send	great street
great soup	great salad	great spot

6. Do this next list silently. Again focus on feeling the position of the tongue. The "s" in these words are close to sounds that require a higher tongue position.

same	hasten	pace	sat
sesame	sassafras	sink	fasten
less	sofa	foster	askance
swift	sister	amiss	septum
lesson	else	sombre	fresco
lease	soon	essential	presence
saint	sensible	essence	psalm
blessing	trespass	scene	missing
listless	century	tresses	bliss
sent	fester	Styx	sum
cesspool	plus	surmise	unceasingly
pass			

7. Using the same principle of preparing the tongue for the correct position, I've prepared this drill. Go slowly at first and then see how fast you can do it and still retain your clear "s" without a flashing tongue as you say each group of words.

watch sun	watch sit	watch send	watch soon

watch sew	watch saw	watch Sue	
each sun	each sit	each send	each soon
each sew	each saw	each Sue	
teach sun	teach sit	teach send	teach soon
teach sew	teach saw	teach Sue	
peach sun	peach sit	peach send	peach soon
peach sew	peach saw	peach Sue	
reach sun	reach sit	reach send	reach soon
reach sew	reach saw	reach Sue	
catch sun	catch sit	catch send	catch soon
catch sew	catch saw	catch Sue	
beach sun	beach sit	beach send	beach soon
beach sew	beach saw	beach Sue	
pitch sun	pitch sit	pitch send	pitch soon
pitch sew	pitch saw	pitch Sue	

8. Here's some sentences to help reinforce the pattern.

Spot can catch, see?
Pitch some balls to Spot.
Spot will run on the beach soon.
Teach some new tricks to Spot.
Send some friends to watch Sue teach Spot.
Let each reach some chips as they sit and watch.

9. Now practice some sentences you might use in conversations and keep your tongue on target. If these don't fit you, make up some of your own using the words containing "s" that I have used in these sentences:

1. Is your sister still going to school?

2. I'll come as soon as possible.
3. I bought some gas on the way to his house.
4. Tell someone to see me about that, the sooner, the better.
5. That's a serious situation. Better not stand still!
6. What's for supper? Any soup or salad is fine.
7. Are you satisfied that he is doing what's expected?
8. Send me over more of the same thing.
9. Go across the street and several blocks to the right.
10. Stop at the store for some cheese, salami, and other cold cuts.

The research so far shows no carry-over learning from "s" to "l" or "r." Therefore, if your problem is mispronouncing "l" and "r" sounds, working on the "s" won't help. The general exercises for tongue thrust can help because they will increase the flexibility of the tongue needed for "l" and "r." Again, the principle of getting the tongue into the position closest to the sound desired is used. I find "n" works well for "l" and "r." If you learned an oriental language first, you probably have difficulty with these sounds. If you can't make "l" at all, start with the "nose" technique.

1. With your tongue pressed firmly against your gum ridge, make the "n" sound till you run out of breath.
2. Make the "n" sound, then clamp your nostrils tightly closed with thumb and forefinger as you

continue to make the "n." It will change to "l" as soon as you restrict the nose. Practice that to hear the "l" sound you want, if you're not sure of the sound of "l."

3. Now practice these words and make a tight contact between the front of your tongue and the roof of your mouth when making the "l" sound. Don't pause between syllables or words.

manly	only	unless	inlaid
in-law	on-leave	enlarge	unlike
moon-lake	unload	Stanley	enlighten
sign-language	fine-luck	moonlight	thin-lipped
tone-ladder	woman-like	mountain-like	

4. Now say these words. Whisper the word first and then say it loudly.

nail	annual	Reynolds	penalty
flannel	banal	vanilla	panel
final	penal	adrenal	Mona Lisa
Nelly	funnel	tunnel	Manila
			Prunella

5. If you can do the first two exercises, practice this. Open your jaws wide. Tightly press the front of the tongue against your upper gum ridge. Blow. It'll feel strange, but air over the sides of the tongue is part of the "l" sound. Now repeat, but this time say "u," as in moon, instead of blowing. Keeping your tongue in the position against the gum, alternate between blowing and making the "ul."

6. Make the "ul" sound for five seconds. Look in a mirror to make sure you don't let the back of the tongue drop.

7. Open your jaws wide. Tightly press the front of the tongue against the gum ridge and the roof of your mouth, and say "ul ah" ten times slowly. Now try "la-la-la-la-la." If your jaw is moving too, steady it with your thumb and index finger.

8. Move now into some practice with "l" followed by a vowel. Be sure you have your tongue in the correct position before you start each word or syllable. Exaggerate the "l" sound. Make it at least one second long.

leave	lill	lair	lend	lamb	last	larm
lup	lorb	loot	loud	lale	lout	lice
loyal	lold	lick	life	lip	line	lean

9. Here's a practice word list that is designed to help you keep the "l" position going strong. If you have difficulty, back up to the other exercises.

loin	fowl	island	ultimate
foil	also	log	alley
alright	let	troll	lucid
Lollard	tranquil	loud	ridicule
cull	olfactory	trial	else
oleo	ell	land	leash
linotype	heal	pal	soul
oiling	mail	loon	fool
altogether	owlish	throttle	lawn
ailing	lunch	illiterate	
lame	fall	oolong	

10. Practice your "l" in these sentences or make up some that fit your life. Remember, the most important practice is the kind that most closely resembles the conversations you have daily.

1. Let's go out to lunch. I'd like a small salad and a large chocolate eclair.
2. Let me get that for you. I have a couple of dollars to squander.
3. Look out! The light's changed. You'll never make it through the yellow!
4. What else is new? Where are you living? See you later.
5. I'll call you before I come. Leave the hall light on.
6. Live and let live. That's what she always replies.
7. Little does he know about how I feel. At long last I'm alive!
8. A long time ago, I always looked hopefully for mail.
9. It looks like it will rain later. Where's the umbrella?
10. Now listen to me: I don't like that. Let's leave well enough alone!
11. Don't be late! Who likes to wait? Lateness is a personal insult with malicious intent to delay.
12. I like the color of your lipstick. Let me try it on my lips.
13. Lend me a couple of nickels; I've lost my wallet.
14. I've lost or mislaid my glasses. Help me look

for them.
15. Does that Oldsmobile belong to you? You've left your lights on.

The formation of "l" is so visible that I usually have little difficulty in teaching it unless the individual has learned an oriental language first. "R" on the other hand, has many variations in the United States and is often invisible. Good American diction requires arching the back of the tongue while lifting the whole front of the tongue.

In the United States, a variety of "r" sounds are present. In New England, it practically disappears, as in such phrases as "pak the cah," while in Chicago it is so hard that linguists call it the snarling "r." In parts of New York, it can become an "oi" sound, as in "goil" or practically turned into a "w," as in "fowa" for four. In the South, it blends softly into a drawl and sometimes disappears completely at the end of words, as in "taya" for tire. In the Midwest it is obvious and often appears in words originally without it altogether, as in "warsh" for wash.

Another variation of the "r" sound that appears in all regions of the country is the childish substitution of the "w" sound, as in "weal" for real. If it continues in adults, it may be that the membrane under the tongue, the frenum, is so short, thick, or inelastic that it cannot stretch sufficiently to allow the tongue to make the sound quickly. For some adults, the problem is solved after a simple frenum cut is performed by their family doctors. In correcting the problem with exercise, all the work outlined for tongue thrust will supplement the exercises given in this section.

Accurate pronunciation of words containing "r's" is best executed with what is called the "general American r," not its regional counterparts. This general "r" will not sound too improbable to the folks at home nor will it be detected by more cosmopolitan listeners.

1. For good "r" sounds, the entire tongue surface must raise. Work with the tongue tip first with the familiar easy "n" sound. The tongue tip is raised to almost the same elevation for "in" as for "r." Feel that upward movement as you practice these words.

nap	nest	nail	nettle
nice	nudge	napkin	nimble
nasty	nourish	nestle	nervous
nobody	name	night	naked
nothing	nausea	notch	noble
news	niggardly	nerve	note
natural	nomad	nip	notion
niche	narrow	nook	nation
noise	now	notify	neutral
nag	next	knock	nod
nine	novel	narrate	

2. Now practice the "ng" sound, to make the back of the tongue arch for the "n." Say these words and feel the tongue hump as you make a strong "ng." Give that back tongue muscle a good workout.

throNG	toNGue	kiNGly	faNG
loNG	middliNG	stuNG	striNGy
struNG	baNG	huNG	stiNG
haNG	briNG	wroNG	cliNG
thiNG	stroNGhold	startliNG	soNGster
sliNG	slaNG	riNGlet	riNGleader
oraNGutaNG	kiNG	koNG	seemiNGly

189

haNGiNGs	haraNGue	haNGer	goNG
gaNG	buNG	loNGiNGly	wittiNGly
aNGry	tiNGle	biliNGual	aNGular
ENGlish	jiNGle	siNGular	youNGer
youNGest	aNGle	fuNGus	flamiNGo
gaNGrene	extiNGuish	loNGest	ANGlo-Saxon
loNGer	aNGer	coNGregation	coNGress
gaNGlion	isiNGlass	kaNGaroo	maNGangese
spaNGle	buNGle	eloNGate	maNGle
iNGersoll	distiNGuish	wraNGle	shiNGle
fiNGer	huNGer	maNGo	syriNGe
commiNGle	juNGle	aNGuish	taNGle

3. The "ng" put the tongue in "r" territory. Let it now lead the "r" gently into place.

ungracious	ungrateful	ungrounded	ungrazed
ungrammatical	ungarnished	ungarnered	ungorged
ungear	ungovernable	ungraded	ungraced
ungrafted	ungrained	ungratified	

4. By moving into the middle with the help of the "ng" sounds, "r" can now try a front entrance with tip-lift help from the sound "n." "Ng" will keep the arch in back as you slide your "r" into each word.

nnnn	ngggg	rrrrather
nnnn	ngggg	rrrripe
nnn	nnnng	rrrrich
nnn	nnng	rrrrule
nnnn	nnng	rrred
nnnn	nnng	rrreach
nnnn	nnng	rrreal
nnnn	nnnng	rrrroooster
nnnn	nnnng	rrrrill
nnn	nnnng	rrrring
nnn	nnnng	rrreap
nnnn	nnnng	rrrrip
nnnn	nnnng	rrrrist (wrist)

5. You can also take advantage of the "t" and "d" tongue tip raise to beautify your developing "r." If you're in front of a mirror, be sure your lips are stationary during the "r" part of the word. If you see them escaping outward, take hold of your mouth with your thumb and index finger and hold them in for the first two sounds (tr, dr) and push them out for the final sound or sounds.

try	trill	true	tray	trench
troll	tread	trip	tram	trait
tramp	train	trail	tragic	trade
tract	track	trace	trance	trash
trap	trust	trunk	trump	

dry	drench	dream	dray	droll
dread	drew	drip	drill	drum
draft	drag	drink	draw	dreg
drop	drown	drudge	drivel	drive
dress	drought	dreary	dregs	droop
drool	drunk	druggist		

6. Frequently, the lips will round for the "r" position when the brain signals there is an "r" ahead. Try to feel that happen as you say these words.

frame	free	frighten	frustrate	frippery
frog	freak	front	from	freeze
frill	fringe	frisk	fritter	frizz
frock	frolic	frond	frost	froth
fruit	fry	frump	frowzy	froufrou

pray	program	pry	priest	prate
prune	prance	preen	pristine	prince
prance	prank	prattle	preach	precinct
preclude	prefer	prescribe	prose	pretty
prevent	price	prig	prim	prime

191

prior	prize	probe	proceed	proclaim
profane	project	prolong		

bray	brambles	break	branch	bright
brooch	breach	broom	brace	brothel
brood	brittle	britska	British	broadcast
brisket	brilliant	brink	briquette	bronze
bride	broken	broth	bronco	breath
brew	brumal	brick	brief	brigade
brigand	brimmer	brindle	brill	briny
brigadier	brier	bridle	briefcase	bridge
brag	brain	brake	brand	brave
brawl	breadth	breed	breeches	breeze
bribe	brim	brisk	bristle	broach
broad	broil	brood	brook	broom
brother	bruise	brush	brusque	brute
burst	burn	burrow	broker	brunet
brunch	bruin	brume	brunt	bryology
brooch	brocket	brogan	brocade	broccoli
brocatelle	broaden	broadbrim		

thread	three	thrust	threat	thrill
throat	thrall	thrombosis	through	thirst
thorn	thorough	thrash	threw	thrice
thrift	throb	throne	throng	throttle
thrive	thrum	thrust	thresh	threshold
thrips	thirteen	thirty	third	thrasonical
thorax	Thoreau			

7. For many people, the "r" between two vowel sounds is the most difficult to make lovely. Try them slowly at first. If you want a good American "r" sound, don't tense your jaw. Let your tongue and lips gently move through the "r" in these words.

forest	corroborate	around	era
borax	terrible	mirage	extemporaneous
correct	mirror	eerie	lariat
borrow	arid	correspond	already
arrest	caring	every	orange

parrot	sorry	story	very
glory	horrid	morrow	perish
pouring	tyranny	carry	berate

8. Keep that perfect "r" short, soft, and sweet as you end these words.

near	are	or	more	year
wear	far	their	stair	sheer
scar	our	bear	war	dare
spare	pyre	mere	father	damper
mother	tarter	bother	scatter	creator
laser	monster	sender	officer	dealer
cheater	climber	breeder	rather	racer
rasher	minister	recharter	recorder	redeemer
recover	rewarder	riffler	rigor	roadster
roaster	roomer	rustler	sinner	minor
your	chair	for	share	

9. If you live in certain eastern areas, watch out for the "rl" combination. That "r" before "l" is often totally mangled into a vowel sound and the "l" is anything but lovely listening. Repeat these, making a smooth transition from "r" to "l."

yearly	hurling	churlish	purely	early
twirl	garlic	surely	girlish	furlong
merely	hurly	demurely	parley	gnarl
curly	pearl	barley	rarely	

10. In reverse, troubles also occur. Practice these, letting your "l" blend easily into the "r." Then move smoothly to complete the word groups.

railroad	all right	millroad
mail route	small wrist	she'll run

stale rice	stable rations	full ransom
drill right	trial run	soul righteousness
hill rill	ridicule Robert	tranquil ranch
dull rap	trill rapidly	he'll refuse
we'll romp	doll rompers	steel rings
kill rats	cradle rocker	helpful rest
sale rug	millwright	

11. To move the "r" into conversation, practice some phrases and sentences that fit your life. Here are some starters.

1. WRite me when you get aRound to it.
2. Let's get Rolling. We can't affoRd to wait till noon to staRt.
3. WheRe aRe you going? You betteR check the caR's batteRy befoRe you go.
4. WeRe you theRe? RobeRt Roe Really Responds to Rock Records.
5. Right now I'd RatheR not. TomoRRow I'll pRobably feel diffeRently.
6. Just give me a little moRe time. Rushing me Really wRecks my day!
7. If he's youR friend, he's my fRiend too. Send him oveR foR an inteRview.
8. If you'Re in tRouble, you have my numbeR.
9. Don't botheR to call; just dRop it by the stoRe.
10. Did you Really buy a caR foR ChRistmas? OR did you boRRow FRank's?
11. Let's go to the theateR afteR dinneR. Any of youR favoRites is gReat foR me.
12. Please call the childRen, we'Re Ready to

194

leave. The caR is out fRont.

13. I'm going to the RecoRd stoRe.
    TheRe aRe thRee new Releases I
    want to heaR.

14. Do you Realize I Really caRe foR
    heR? It's haRd foR me to expRess it
    in woRds.

15. Let's go hoRseback Riding this Sat-
    uRday afternoon. WeaR youR Rain
    geaR!

Unless you want to be identified with a particular region of the country, sound the "r" lightly and go right on. Otherwise you'll have hung a tag around your neck that says "New England," "New York," "South," or "Midwest." Even though you have improved all of your other sounds, and have worked on the pitch, resonance, and intensity, your "r" can muddle your efforts and mangle your style.

If you're not sure that you have developed the "r" that you want for you style, enlist the help of a friend whose speech you admire. Ask the person to record the sentences on a tape. Leave a five-second lapse between each sentence group. Count one thousand one through one thousand five silently between the sentence groups. When you are alone and can concentrate completely on listening, play the tape and stop it after each sentence group. Try to repeat each sentence as you heard it without referring to the list. Your brain will gradually tune all parts involved in making the fine motor movement and produce the sounds as they are heard. Twenty minutes a day for one week eliminated "r" distortions completely for one man whose Bostonian accent was not appreciated by his west coast employer who was considering promoting him. The amount of time you need may be less. You can check the progress by taping the sentences yourself, exactly as your friend did, and then comparing the tapes sentence by sentence. This takes time, especially if you have one recorder and have to switch tapes back and forth, but remember that studies show over and over again that involvement in practice of a behavior is the key to achieving it.

This chapter completes your work on developing skills and refining your voice power. Now consider how you can expand your use of voice into more of your life. Studies of the winners in life — happy, successful, prosperous people — show that they are always involved in transforming others. Perhaps using your voice power to exert a positive effect on the lives of those less fortunate than you is the way to make voice power a way of life. The next chapter will present some exciting suggestions for making voice power your life-style.

TEN

Making Voice Power into a Life-style

After all the hard work that you have been engaged in recently, training your voice so that it is the best that it can be at all times and is a part of your total image, it is now time to be sure that it is really a focal point in every facet of your life-style. Without realizing it, you may only have concentrated on incorporating your new-found vocal acuity in just one or two parts of your many roles, ignoring the rest. However, remember that the more you consciously work to use your voice properly, the better it will be overall.

Now is also a time to think about areas open to you that weren't before. A powerful, clear, effective voice does not just mean improvement in your present life. Careers and hobbies that concentrate on or use your new voice power are a real possibility for you now, and you may want to take advantage of them. Avocations, hobbies, careers, and new ways of participating in religious, social, and recreational organizations are all possible for the person who has developed a powerfully effective voice and enthusiastically integrates it into his or her life-style.

Of course your voice has always been a part of your life-style, but you haven't realized this, nor taken full advantage of it. Now that you know the tremendous potential in your voice, you have many ways to let your life reflect the whole you, the best you, through your main projector, voice.

The most available opportunity to use your new voice skills is in sales. Select some product you really have found useful and commit yourself to selling it part-time for a month. Most of my students are shocked by that suggestion (except of course, those who are already in sales work). They really don't feel capable of selling anything.

Yet, I've never had a single person who was not a salesman in any of my classes. *We all are.* We're constantly convincing ourselves of our own ideas. And whether we know it or not, we're also constantly selling ourselves to others. If you are desperately afraid of persuading others, you may be just as afraid of persuading yourself. Persuading yourself to take action is the most critical part of using the power you have. As soon as you can do that, you should have no problem in selling an idea or a product to others. We are all human; we have a scared, weak part and also a basically strong part. Confidently share your ideas about a product to another person, he or she will pick up your positive feeling about communication and appreciate it, whether buying or not. Your voice, not your words, gives the basic clues that are acted upon by others. It represents your honesty as well as your power.

When I speak of power in the broad sense, I mean power over yourself, not over others. The power to transform yourself has a greater potential than any you will ever have over the lives of others. As soon as you take the steps to use that power, your whole personality and life-style can change if you want it to. Your greatest source of available power is your own voice, and now that you have explored its depths and heights, it is possible to move into a style of life that transforms you, and in the process it can transform all those around you.

In chapter 5, we discussed how your voice plays a dramatic role in your self-image. If you have not strengthened your self-image, this will be reflected in the loudness, timing, intensity, and resonance focus of your voice. In addition, use of voice power utilizes expression of feeling. It is almost impossible to sell something, be it a product, idea, or attitude, to someone else if you're not committed to it yourself. Even the most clever, practiced salesmen cannot fool all of the people all of the time.

Once my acting class was given the ideas held by a particular character. We were then instructed, while seated, to demonstrate through quality, timing, pitch, resonance, intonation, loudness, pronunciation, diction, and breathing, the character's interpretation of those ideas. But we could use no real words—only gibberish. The remainder of the class wrote down which set of ideas was being expressed. There were no errors; everyone understood the message without body action or words.

Pick out one of the phrases on the self-image test in chapter 8. In nonsense words, express the idea with your voice. Then try expressing the exact opposite. If you can't spontaneously speak in gibberish, say such phrases as "that's hard to believe," "you're so loving," or "that's terrible."

Since you want to enhance your involvement in your daily life on all levels, you are concerned with sharing genuine feeling. In order to do this, you *must* be ready to share your conclusions with others. For example, it may be risky in a job to take a firm stand on a particular issue, but if you have researched it carefully and know what you are talking about, you will be more successful taking a firm, positive approach. Even if your idea is not accepted, you will be regarded as a responsible, involved person whose opinion is to be respected. This is obviously better than being discounted because you are undecided on most issues.

One good exercise that demonstrates the transforming power of feeling in voice is one I learned in an acting class. Write each word backwards and then scramble them into a new order and read them aloud. For example, convey with your voice timing, loudness, pitch, intensity, intonation, and color the meaning of a phrase like "I have free my thinking of old resentments of persons or situations," and "I have *not* freed my thinking of old resentments of persons and situations." (In gibberish, that might be: Woo Dreef evah kingnith toy mentassenter dol fo sonsper fo nationsit ro.) Once you fully realize what message you send out through your voice, you will be ready to take the necessary steps to bring your best voice power into your life-style.

For many, this book will be the only step that is needed. They have known all along the power of their voice and probably have said over and over again, "I already do that. I know that!" as they read about the various parts of voice. For them, the information has just pointed up some ways of improving on what they're already using.

Others may not and you may be among them. You may feel you've only scratched the surface and need more help. If further practice of the exercises in this book doesn't seem sufficient, you might want to seek professional help.

You have reached the point of realizing that training for your voice is not irrelevant to your life. Maybe the greatest growth you have made is in your willingness to continue to look for ways to improve your voice. For many people, however, seeking help in school is not the solution. Some of their most unpleasant memories are tied up with teachers, schools, and discomfort among other students (where perhaps they learned some of their worst voice habits). What are the other alternatives for those who need more guidance?

Before you take any step, consider what you would like as the ultimate result of training. If you want to develop artistic qualities associated with performance, it means more training in the use of resonance, pitch, timing, intonation, quality with the focus on carrying power, versatility, control, and serviceability. You can explore that alternative by seeking out acting lessons, a drama class, or an oral interpretation class.

If you want the skill of being able to talk before small groups, such as those at your church, lodge or club, you can develop it through the Toastmasters and Toastmistress programs. Although the goals are different for the groups, both are open to men and women, and warm friendly help is their highlight. For your closest local chapter, write Toastmasters International, 2200 North Rand Avenue, P.O. Box 10400, Santa

Ana, California, 92711 or Toastmistress International, 9068 Firestone Boulevard, Downey, California 90241.

You may have no interest in talking before groups but merely have a lot of trouble in just *finding* words. You may lack the time to read more widely as most authorities suggest, find it hard to sit down and work through a vocabulary building book, or be unable to sit down to relax and read at home because you're always reminded of all the things you've left undone. A dynamic vocabulary course could be the answer.

Pure vocabulary courses are hard to find. Ethna Reid, nationally known reading specialist, often gives an early morning vocabulary course for people who have a full busy day. The course is an hour once a week at 7 A.M. in Salt Lake City, Utah. You can write Ms. Reid at the Exemplary Center for Reading, 2888 Highland Drive, Salt Lake City, Utah, 84116. Her ideas on vocabulary development evolved from the research she did to discover why children failed to learn to read in special remedial reading classes, and these findings have been used to successfully revolutionize the teaching of all elementary subjects. If anyone can show you how to expand your word knowledge and usage, Ethna can! If you don't live near Salt Lake City, you might look for a speed reading class.

Most speed reading classes include vocabulary development programs. Pushing you to increase your reading rate is the main goal, but in order to do that, you will need to understand more words quickly. Some reading courses train the mind to absorb a whole page with one glance. The person focuses on no specific words. In this type of course vocabulary development as a distinct need is not believed essential. You grasp the ideas from the context, not from the few unfamiliar words. All year throughout the country, Alpha Awareness offers reading training without vocabulary emphasis but with the goal of improving many areas to build confidence and success. They will send you specific information from their home office, 630 Parkdale, Susanville, California, 96130, if you feel this will meet your need to read more to expand your word contacts and your reservoir of information.

Other resources are available to move a voice power vocabulary block. Adult education classes through a community college, private language arts programs, reading institutes, "free" schools, extension courses from universities all are prospective sources of more word prowess through reading or vocabulary instruction.

If difficulty in speaking clearly and articulating certain sounds correctly is your problem, then contact the American Speech and Hearing Association for names of nearby individuals or clinics that are especially trained to help you solve those problems. Their new headquarter's address is 10801 Rockville Pike, Rockville, Maryland, 20852.

A career that concentrates on helping others overcome voice power problems can be a satisfying life's work. As a speech pathologist, I wholeheartedly believe that the dynamic interplay between the therapist and client is the most exciting way of learning. I not only help others to open up and expand their power, but I learn constantly more about my own strengths and weaknesses. I don't know of a more invigorating career field than human communication. Every time I help a deaf child to speak those first words, or guide a stroke victim back to speech, or participate in the growth of someone in finding the power in their voice, I experience so much joy that I want to encourage everyone to share in our profession's work of developing, expanding, and enhancing communication. If you are searching for a voice power career, write to the American Speech and Hearing Association for information on our profession and the training programs available.

In some states, the position of speech aide is available, which has no set educational requirements and encompasses a wide range of activities with a speech professional. I find enthusiastic speech aides invaluable in assisting me with groups of small children, monitoring exercises with adult voice improvement classes, and putting into practice some of the gadgets and devices I contrive to motivate children to enjoy language learning. Speech aides also type, dust and clean up the messes the children and I make in our therapy sessions. We both share and benefit in working with all ages and kinds of people.

But perhaps, for you, voice power in your life-style has a different meaning. It could be a career in politics. It is something to consider seriously even if you've rejected it wholeheartedly in the past. Consider the experience of one of my voice improvement class members. Her husband, at the time, held a political office. Before the seven-week class session ended, he suddenly died. At first she was shocked when confronted by the suggestion that she run for the remainder of his term. We discussed whether she could move quickly out of the weeping widow role and into an active political life. Her doubts transformed into zeal as she discovered how much she did know about her husband's job, and that she did want to continue his work as the only black member of certain committees. All she had learned in class had to be used immediately. She won the election and has continued to be politically active as part of the new voice power style of her life. She feels at home in organized politics.

To many, organized politics is tainted by the possibility of unwanted control from distant bosses. Voice power people usually enjoy "unorganized politics." That's my two-word summary that describes working on something you believe needs to happen *for* people. Are you against income taxes? Think battered wives deserve protection and shelter? How about the lonely, poverty-stricken situation of many of our elderly? One of my most fearless unaffiliated politicians believes that churches misuse their tax-exempt status. He speaks wherever he can, presenting information, opinion, and determination to bring about change. With a powerful voice that makes full use of timing, resonance, and loudness variations, he presents his message. He works full-time at a lackluster job, but runs an ad in the paper stating his availability to speak without fee on "Should Churches Continue To Be Tax Exempt?" His joy in life is the rich anticipation that comes with each new speaking engagement. The question and answer period after his talk gives him a chance to fully explore the possibilities of his voice and his control over it. His voice dynamics have become the major vehicle for his action-provoking message. Armed with a list of facts about the holdings of churches, he is not disarmed by the anger and disbelief he encounters. In fact, he says it energizes him and his delivery becomes even better! The potential for conflict and controversy is only present in a few voice power opportunities. Even those who have chosen street corner or door to door religious persuasion tell me they find little opposition.

For those who want to use their voice power for grateful, loving recipients, try reading for the blind. Braille cannot take the place of another caring person, particularly if the reader can express shades of meaning beyond what "holes in paper" can. Some organizations make cassette recordings for the blind of whole books and use readers. Nursing homes frequently have elderly blind who would come alive with your rendition of some of the features in the newspaper that usually are not converted to Braille. (Those who are not blind would like it, too.) Starting in a one-to-one situation with a handicapped person is a good way to start practicing voice power if you're shy. If you're not, then you're ready for a bigger step.

How about becoming a docent, an unpaid specialized teacher. You qualify if you are over sixteen and like to enthusiastically talk about animals, birds, trees, railroad history, art of all kinds, or about anything you might find in a zoo, arboretum, museum, art gallery, court room, park, science room, nature center, or observatory. For the docent program, you volunteer time once a week to lead tours, talk to classes, give on-the-spot demonstrations, or assist in the sponsored activities. Of course in the beginning, that day a week is spent in training, which could include anything from attending a class to learn about King Tut's life and the art of that time to getting the facts about the mating habits of apes. Each institution has its own training programs to fit the needs of the facility in working with the public's desire for information. You're encouraged to help research material and to be creative in your interpretations. You have the backup of paid staff to expand your knowledge and guide you in working with the varied groups of visitors. Working with the public as a guide and teacher is the ideal setting to allow your voice power to season into mastery.

In Sacramento a docent program is being developed for the railroad museum built as part of the reconstruction of old Sacramento as it was in the Gold Rush days. I can envision the needed docents as being everything from railroad buffs who recognize every old train whistle to young people who have discovered the adventure of railroading through films and books. They'll revel in explaining the colorful background of railroad fact and legend and provide a needed service too. One of the planners told me handicapped people are encouraged to train for the program too; the main requirement is enthusiasm and a desire to share. If you are interested in a docent program, you should consult the directory compiled by the American Association of Museums available at large libraries for a list of all the museums. No doubt you'll discover some very unique opportunities to learn about rare collections you never dreamed existed. If you want to skip the directory, you can call any park, zoo, or museum near you and ask if they use docents: if not, tell them you'd like to volunteer your time to help in a docent capacity and would also like to participate in gathering background materials and setting up activities to expand the public's use of their facility. Here's a specific opportunity to use what you know about voice power to *sell yourself*; if they're suspicious, don't worry. It's only because they lack information about you or have not been sufficiently creative to expand their services through developing a docent program. Tell them about the two docent organizations functioning in California: Southern California Docent League (Los Angeles County Museum of Natural History, 900 Exposition Boulevard, Los Angeles, California, 90007), and the Docent Forum (San Jose Historical Museum, 635 Phelan Avenue, San Jose, California, 95112). Although there is no national organization, docents across the country meet to share the excitement of their discoveries and to learn still more about making ear- and eye-stimulating presentations.

The commitment to give your time to teach is really a commitment to expand your usage of the power available in your voice. Most of my students think they are too busy to give any time to a project like this on a regular basis. However, when they look closely at what fills their lives now, they discover that they can choose to take out something unpleasantly inessential and put a more satisfying choice in its place. Some have learned to watch the section that advertises for volunteers in their newspapers. Here they find a gold mine of opportunities to practice voice power, as well as their new self-image of friendly, assertive competence.

In addition, through volunteering, you may find yourself moving toward a new career from your new contacts. Alvin Tofler of *Future Shock* fame has predicted we may all change careers as many as five times in a life span as our society continues to discard old functions and take on new ones. With your fully developed voice power, you're prepared for that, particularly with the advance in technology for recording the voice that has sparked the development of new industries. From talking toy animals for children to a device for your telephone that lets you know if your caller is lying to you, this has become the voice age of industry too. Now that you are aware of what your voice can mean to you, you may choose to become involved with the burgeoning voice equipment industry, such as visual and auditory feedback instruments.

In the 1960s I was eagerly testing the using of an auditory feedback instrument with retarded children at Fairview State Hospital in California. This instrument played back what was said every four seconds (or a time you select) and made it possible for children to immediately compare their production of a word with mine. The earphones captured and amplified the word right in their heads, and the fun of speaking into a microphone and hearing their voices all merged into change-producing feedback. Think of the possibilities that evolved from this single instrument in helping people with voice, dialect, or articulation deficiencies. Machines that can show you if you have made a good or defective "s," "r," or other specific sound are being marketed by people from many backgrounds invigorated by the fervor for voice-improvement products.

Prints showing the tones of the voice in the frequencies of pitches are produced by complex machines and used by police, singers, deaf children, and also by people who have voice problems. The volume of research that has resulted from these instruments has contributed to our knowledge in innumerable scientific areas. You can become a part of research such as the kind that has shown how study of the voice prints of cries of newborn infants can tell us if they have brain malfunction or thyroid deficiency. To learn more about voice prints, sonograms, or spectograms, I visited one of the largest companies manufacturing these instruments, Kay Elemetrics in Pinebrook, New Jersey. I brought tapes of some people with chronically hoarse voices and some of singers' voices. I wanted to better understand their problems by seeing the picture of the frequencies they automatically use to produce their voices.

While I was there, two of the staff returned from demonstrating their equipment at a school for the deaf. They were so excited to report watching a deaf child finally attain the accurate pronunciation of the word "telephone" through seeing on the instrument the difference between the incorrect emphasis and the correct pattern. Can you imagine how intriguing continuous involvement with these instruments could be with daily new uses and new research? Maybe this is the direction you want to go with your voice power.

The voice scientists using the instruments are having a field day. There is so much research to be done in the area of singing alone that it will take years to fill the information gaps. Many of the ideas voice teachers have used to teach singing are without basis in fact, according to the new research in voice laboratories. For example, respiratory physiologist Thomas Hixon's studies are showing that singers can breathe better while singing with their abdomens hanging out instead of the traditional tucked-under-the-rib-cage position. Hixon explains that during rib-cage lifting in singing, with the stomach tucked under it, the singer unknowingly attempts to inhale while exhaling. We shall undoubtedly hear greater voices with more intricate subtleties of tones when all of the facts about how the respiratory muscles can best perform during singing are discovered by voice power scientists. With a family of singers around me, one of whom is studying for an operatic career, I consider the field of acoustical research an exhilarating outlet for an interest in voice power.

I asked Ingo Titze, who has been involved in voice research at Gallaudet College for the deaf and at the University of Iowa, to recommend training programs for those interested in finding out more about careers in voice science. He said prospective students should explore the programs at Brigham Young University, the Michigan Institute of Technology, and some other major universities. Dr. Titze's research on how well the vocal tissue is able to use the energy in the breath stream has gained national recognition. According to his study, about 1 percent of the energy is used to produce sound. When more was used during stress, the temperature of the vocal folds increased. They became less elastic and inflamed. Eventually a change in the tissue itself resulted and, of course, a change in voice. Voice laboratories where these experiments were performed are part of the voice age opportunities for the scientist-singer, whose knowledge of the intricacies of controlling the voice for difficult singing helps him effectively plan and carry out needed research. (Dr. Titze had just completed singing a role in *Die Fledermaus* when I talked to him.) The voice experiment field offers a possibility for a singer to make a scientific contribution after stopping strenuous full-time singing. As a part of acoustical science, it offers music majors more employment options than a pure music concentration.

Another opportunity to put your voice power to work is teaching a self-help class. Pick out a course that really intrigues you. Everything from massage techniques to memory development is offered in flyers posted at libraries, markets, and other public bulletin boards. Take a course to prepare now to teach it, and jot down all the ways the course could be improved by better use of voice power. Discuss your preparation for teaching the course with the instructor. For many courses, there are special seminars for future teachers of the material. Most of them require no special college background, but do require an enthusiastic familiarity with the course work and some skill in presenting it to groups. Of course this means learning to use your voice in a dramatic and personal way to bring the information convincingly and beneficially to your audience. When students complain that they didn't benefit from a class, the instructor's use of voice was at least partially at fault. Impact from materials can happen best when there is impact in the voice. Without good use of melody, timing, loudness, resonance, diction, and pronunciation, boredom rather than learning usually occurs.

The possibility of bringing depth to your teaching increases when you design the program yourself! You can create and market a course from your own special interest. One organization in Sacramento, California, Learning Time, markets home courses for their teachers. The course description and fees are printed in a small newspaper that is distributed to supermarkets and other places where they can be picked up free by consumers. The class size usually is limited to the number the teachers can accommodate in their own home, although some are located in larger settings. The organization handles enrollments and fees with a percentage of this paid to the teacher.

Although at first you may not make much money, you will gain presentation skills dramatically. Each class will become better as you learn how to fully use your voice to enliven your information. One study demonstrated that students forget 85 percent of the material taught them. Keep that in mind as you consider teaching a class you design. Exciting vocal presentation could substantially improve this discouraging figure in your class, whether it be Early Mandolin or Late Chinese Cookery.

Developing a class to teach a musical instrument requires much voice effort to retain interest while students are learning playing skills. If you don't make an animated effort to project enthusiasm when demonstrating the instrument, you will not generate the motivation for long hours of practice. Students give up quickly when daily practice is required, and they realize it is impossible to fake it when they've skipped. Rather than admit to a teacher they have not practiced, they quit. Although teaching an instrument you know sounds like the easiest way to expand your voice power in teaching, it turns out to be one of the most difficult. It takes more than knowledge to teach — and more than voice power to act.

Little theater groups can offer opportunities for exciting experimentation for the use of voice. Reader's plays in which you don't memorize lines or cues are an easier alternative if you're a little reticent to become involved in more elaborate productions. Churches, lodges, service clubs of all kinds are beginning to use plays to present concepts as well as entertain their membership, and you can take the initiative by suggesting a reader's play to the program chairman. Of course, any play can become a "reader's play." You can also form your own group and after much practice offer it to the public for a price. Modern well-known plays poignantly read from a round-table setting provide an excellent opportunity for exhilarating, inspired use of your new voice. All of the readers' energies go into the voice interpretation of the role rather than being channeled into action of characters as in ordinary play productions. Since you need not use costumes or scenery, expenses are minimum. Another advantage is that during the performance you continue to use a script marked for phrasing, pausing, intensity, quality changes, rate changes, special intonation effects, and loudness changes. With guiding marks, a beginner is not likely to "go dead" before his audience.

Another kind of reader's play is the old-time radio dramas, which use sound effects with gusto to embellish the efforts of the actors. Off the scene for years, radio drama has eased its way back in many areas of the country. Although it will probably never again reach the zenith of popularity of the forties or provide the acting career opportunities of that era, small stations can still offer this option. With the constant expansion of AM and FM radio stations, announcing, disc jockeying, and running talk shows have burgeoned all over the country. The dream of saying, "This is the news," may not be such an unrealistic goal if, in the beginning, you can be content with a 5000-watt radio station in Bo-peepsia. The background of people working at these one-man stations is varied. Some have graduated from radio schools and others from university training programs, and all must have a first-class engineer's license, since these jobs may include running electronic equipment. However, I learned from one reputable radio school director that people as young as fourteen have been able to master the information required for a license.

Some stations have time available for unsponsored, unpaid features. This is an ideal opportunity to create your own shows. All you need is a theme around which to build your material. Unusual animal stories, local history, unusual recipes, how-to shows, and interviews with colorful local people can build into a fifteen-minute spot. Poetry reading, dramatic interpretations of contemporary or classical literature, and serialized reports on a current topic of general interest are all good choices for developing your own program, an outlet for your voice personality.

Another good outlet for a career in radio is selling commercials. Every radio station's big product is "time for sale" and that takes a staff of persuasive people to convince prospective advertisers that sales will increase through radio promotion. Selling through using your voice power is probably one of the best paid careers available without a college background. The income of sales people usually exceeds what is paid many college-educated professionals. Using your voice to sell is a highly marketable skill and, of all the possibilities for the use of voice power, direct sales work is the most demanding. Belief in your product is reflected in voice color, as well as in timing, phrasing, intensity, and so on. If dissatisfaction with employer or wages transfers on some level to your product, the customer will respond to this unspoken message as well as the spoken one. In other words, they get a double message that causes hesitation about the purchase, even though they may want the product.

Voice cues are so subtle that they often escape analysis. However, we are all experts in using them and in disregarding the actual words. Training in this skill begins in infancy when words mean nothing and voice means everything. We could predict our parents actions by the intensity, pitch changes, rate changes, and emotional color even before we could speak ourselves. We also learned early when they meant business, or when it was a pretended threat. That voice reading training can continue to help you in all sales work. Listening for the cues in a customer's voice and responding to those messages, as well as the words, makes sales work an intriguing interaction, especially in selling for a radio station.

If you don't think you have the courage to face another human being who might turn you down, telephone sales work might be an easier first step in your voice power career. The telephone survey in the first chapter is useful as a training technique. Since you aren't marketing any product, there is much less pressure, and you gain experience in person-to-person presentation. Talking on the telephone is a skill many people do not have, simply because they lack voice power understanding and voice power skills. Telephone selling is an extensive enterprise in this country (and almost unheard of in all others). Recently I've bought sittings at a photographer, a coupon book for a variety of services, a trial series at a local health club, and tickets for benefits, all as the result of convincing telephone sales. I have turned down magazine offers, cosmetic sales, two newspaper subscription pitches, several other requests for donations of various kinds, and solicitations for advertisements in the yellow pages of telephone directories of several nearby communities. People who do this sales work out of their own homes are in demand, and many other companies have gigantic telephone switchboards that require dozens of sales voices.

Any true advocate of voice power will not consider telephone selling an intrusion on sacred domestic privacy and will allow a fellow human being the opportunity to make a living through a telephone sales contact. Since many of the most memorable conversations of my life have occurred over the telephone, I wholeheartedly endorse its use for sales as well as for those special moments of deep communication through all the nuances of voice. Telephone operators daily receive immediate reactions to their voice power image. Lily Tomlin's humorous Ernestine burlesque of the bitchy operator's voice struck home to millions of phone users. We all empathize with the prerogative of power the operator has when we don't have another dime. Ernestine shows us the bottom line of voice power. She exudes contempt and arrogant superiority, as she coldly flouts her power, sneering and snorting vindictive answers to a pitifully frustrated victim. A career as a telephone operator does indeed lend itself to practicing the best and the worst in voice power.

The switchboard operator at many large institutions can give the whole facility a disparaging reputation. A secretary can make a whole office appear ineffective and unresponsive by his or her voice communication to incoming calls. Usually a secretary is totally unaware of being the pivot that can subvert the reputation of a whole cluster of competent workers. This negative functioning cannot be detected on a performance rating scale since the person may fulfill every category satisfactorily: answers phone courteously, gives information correctly and properly, speaks clearly and audibly. However, the rate of speech, use of pauses, intensity variation, use of color, and so on, speak more loudly than words.

From the funeral home operator to the man at the gas pump, many other jobs are actually careers in voice power. Even if you are unable to move into another job now, you can reflect the very best in voice power on your present job.

Keeping your voice on target by realizing your responsibility for its care and development is another part of your commitment to voice power. The next chapter will guide you toward avoiding misuse and vocal abuse.

ELEVEN

Protecting Your
Vocal Instrument

Without realizing it, you are probably guilty of vocal abuse — not toward others, but toward the delicate membranes of tissue deep in your throat.

You've probably listened to the voices of older people and hoped you wouldn't sound like that some day. Many times what you are hearing is vocal fatigue, catching up after years of incorrect voice use. You know other older people who don't sound that way. You can protect yourself from developing the effortful voice of the aged speaker by managing your precious communicative instrument effectively now. If you're already in the tired voice syndrome, it's never too late to remedy the situation.

You wouldn't ignore warning signs of a torn-up road. You'd slow down and probably turn around. It isn't difficult to learn to pay attention to common signs that you're headed for voice trouble.

Most often voice damage is temporary, caused by occasional yelling at a sporting event, a loss of temper, or attempting to get someone's attention over a long distance. The tissues usually recover after a few hours and, if not aggravated too soon after, remain in good condition.

However, many people have frequent problems with hoarseness, and they haven't been yelling at football games or anyplace else. They have not learned to speak with a relaxed voice. Their daily misuse of the vocal tissue by banging them together with too much consistent intensity and perhaps in the wrong pitch, can cause nodules, contact ulcers, and other serious problems.

Some jobs are perfect setups for patterns of vocal abuse. George worked in a machine shop, and frequently could not make it home unless he stopped for a few stout ones with the boys. At work, to compete with the noise level, George had to talk loudly and shout most of the day, and he felt he needed a few smokes, a few jokes, and a few jiggers of gin to help him unwind before facing his wife and children. Gradually he became noticeably hoarse by the end of the day, but he treated it with a whiskey remedy handed down by a buddy's grandmother. George woke up one morning and could talk only in a whisper. On his vocal folds, the doctor found reddened tissue and two nodules facing each other. They were easily removed, George recovered quickly, and started back to work. He could hardly wait to greet his buddies at the bar. Three months later, George again gradually became hoarse. You guessed it: more nodules. Voice strain at work, plus the effects of smoke and alcohol in constricting the blood vessels were the perfect ingredients for a double batch of nodules. Unless George breaks this cycle, the consequences could become worse.

The histories of many clients who have undergone surgery for cancer of the vocal tissue show the same pattern: voice strain, habitual smoking, and drinking. The only positive aspect of this kind of cancer is that it usually stays localized in the throat and does not generally spread throughout the body. In a very small percentage of cases, treatment other than complete removal of the vocal tissue and any other cancerous tissue is successful.

I personally know of only one case in twenty years of practice in which the vocal tissue did not have to be removed, which means total loss of voice. I share that information with you in the hope that you truly recognize the possible serious consequences of vocal abuse and how to counteract them. A personal friend who had formerly assisted me in speech therapy groups developed the cancer seven years after I had left the hospital where we worked together. Her new position was working in a vocally demanding role teaching severely retarded clients. She was a moderate smoker (in spite of my nagging) but most of her drinking was pink lemonade, and that was always available in her refrigerator (could lemonade be irritating to abused tissue?). The familiar pattern of an extended period of hoarseness, followed by the discovery and removal of nodules and eventually the terrifying diagnosis of cancer shocked all of us close to her. As you might suspect, speech pathologists have a habit of looking after the voices of friends, scolding, advising, and hopefully protecting them from the consequences of voice strain. How sobering it is when a vocal disaster occurs in spite of their efforts. But my friend escaped surgery.

The final step of the pattern, total removal of the larynx, was never carried out after the decision to do so had been made. The physician decided to have a final look at the cancerous folds, which had been paralyzed by the disease for some time. To his surprise he observed movement. This was enough to warrant trying X-ray therapy instead of surgery. But what started that movement? Why would tissues overcome and overrun by cancer, and perhaps still not recovered from nodule surgery, be able to function at all? This friend saved her voice through her own powerful, directed thoughts and positive attitude. However, this is not a simple task and I know of many others who are headed for vocal problems who lack her persistance and discipline.

For example, one of my friends lost her voice while conscientiously trying to train a new puppy not to chew unchewables. Another, a competent mother of eight, is chronically hoarse. Managing eight active children is vocally demanding unless you sleep through it. A medical student donned a lion's costume and roared around a playing field as a mascot for several seasons. He has been gravel-voiced for years. Another young friend enjoys rock concerts and has bouts of hoarseness afterwards. Her enthusiastic joining in the singing and screaming are part of the excitement in life she doesn't want to miss. A male friend, who like his father, lowers his chin and speaks in a voice below his natural pitch, now has developed the habit of frequent throat clearing. The continuous low voice strain has produced dryness and redness. Like frequent yelling and talking loudly, throat clearing is damaging to the vocal membranes, and opens the door to more serious problems.

Problems with voice often can be traced to personal attitudes and beliefs that create tension. As I've discussed earlier, it is difficult to use your voice efficiently when the body is not relaxed. The cause of the tension is sometimes so subtle that you may not be aware of it. You may also have come to adapt to a certain constant state of tension without even realizing it.

In the above examples of behavior that caused voice difficulties, there are indications that some of the people were so overly concerned with achieving a certain image that they were unnecessarily excessive in their actions. The puppy trainer may not have needed as much voice power, but the need for control over her dog impelled her to overreact. The same attitude could be at work with the man who unknowingly adopted the posture and voice of his father. The additional strain on my friend's voice when she was assigned a difficult class as well as the need to be authoritative were potent causes underlying the development of nodules and cancer.

Money—its acquisition and the things it can buy—and status are at the top of the list of tension producers. Now would be a good time to explore your own attitudes toward money. If you find that you tend to have a fear of spending it, miserliness, coupled with a belief that you really must struggle to get or hang on to it, are afraid or embarrassed to accept it even when it is due you, or believe that it is the key to happiness, or even unhappiness and un-Godliness, you have given power to money that can overrun your life. You may very well discover that when you have thoughts about money, you hear in your words the tension that is spreading through your body.

I find that people who abuse their voices frequently have distorted feelings about money. Helping them identify these attitudes and giving them some new ways to deal with the getting and giving process usually removes a great deal of this stress. Here are the suggestions that have been most effective in creating a new awareness of security and prosperity.

1. Train yourself not to think or say "I can't afford it" to explain lacks. This is programming a belief that there is a continuous shortage of certain things in your life. Your subconscious will subdue any thoughts or activities that would make this belief incorrect.

2. Look directly at anyone paying you, take their money in your hands, and say warmly, "Thank you very much." Do not reinforce embarrassment concerning money by quickly putting it aside and changing the subject. If you give embarrassment or other uncomfortable feelings in return for payment you discourage it.

3. Counter destructive clichés about money, whether they're repeated by yourself or others. Typical are: money spoils children, rich people are unhappy, God loves only the poor, money brings troubles.

4. Stop excusing your purchases by saying, "I got it on sale." Give up "It was a bargain," "It was half-price, marked down," or "It needed repair." If you need to exaggerate and reinforce your need for constant thrift in buying, you reinforce an image of lack of money.

5. When you buy items on sale, say firmly, "This is the correct price for this item that I need and can easily afford." Forget bragging to friends or salving your conscience with excuses.

6. Stop giving yourself double messages about money. Never spend to save, or use the words "have to buy" or "should save." Always buy for the real reason: you wanted the item. Putting the responsibility on some unnamed force compelling you to replace tires, fill your tank with gas, or put money in the bank muddles the truth that you are a responsible financial manager.

7. Pay your bills with a smile, and if writing checks, say to yourself, "I gratefully pay this bill." If you receive checks from others, put a "thank you" as well as your signature on the back. Expressing gratefulness for any financial exchange adds a positive color that will spread and eventually return to you.

8. Discuss fees openly and immediately when seeking services. If you do not have the money to meet the costs, state that as a fact without apology. If the service is indispensable, suggest an exchange of some kind. Never allow yourself to feel guilty about not having money.

9. Never refuse a gift of money, and do not hesitate to give money no matter how small the amount. Acquire the habit of giving easily to causes and charities in which you believe. The exact value of what you are willing to give will return to you not only in terms of money, but love and service.

10. Do not hoard or hide money. Remember it is only a medium of exchange, and as such is neither good nor bad, filthy nor clean. Acting miserly, avoiding bills, complaining about prices, and so forth, feed your unconscious stress reservoir, whose eruption can cause many difficulties.

A body cannot tell the difference between stress created by money worries and other emotional thoughts and stress created by infections, surgery, wounds, burns, injuries, allergic reactions, severe exertion, malnutrition, and severe exposure to heat, cold, or sun. Dr. Hans Selye proved conclusively that the body reacts the same way and sends out exactly the same hormones to combat them. Selye, who holds doctorates in science, medicine, and in biochemistry, is known as the Father of the Concept of Stress.

All disease starts with an alarm reaction to stress, and in many cases the reaction to stress occurring during any inflammation becomes the disease itself (arthritis, bursitis, colitis, nephritis, allergies, laryngitis). Paying more attention to body signals could eliminate many health problems. According to Dr. Selye, these signals can be used to achieve the right balance in your life. Learning to provide activities to release built-up tension can prevent "stressitis" conditions from developing. He described the two kinds of hormones that we all produce as syntoxic and catatoxic. The syntoxic type are the cortisone group. Because their flow increases when we are relaxed, Selye called them the hormones of harmonious cooperation. When we are under stress, whether it's worry or a gunshot wound, catatoxic hormones rush to meet our need. Many people's bodies continuously secrete catatoxic hormones because they feel pushed, hurried, and unable to keep up with the pace of those around them. Eventually, the body's organs can no longer tolerate the speeding up of so many of their processes and illness results. Learning to direct energy appropriately through a crash course in assertiveness has been a godsend to some. Sometimes the voice strain habit pattern becomes even worse during assertiveness training courses because the person is trying so hard to use the newly learned principles that he or she is talking more—and more intensely.

One of my best attended talks in the voice power series is titled "Who Wrong with You and How to Wing it Through." Winging it through is not easy for people with voice problems. Vocally they are usually strong actors and reactors, I developed my suggestions from the lectures, talks, tapes, books, and interaction with favorite, outstanding teachers from the fields of psychiatry, psychology, physics, medicine, education, health, parapsychology, and religion, over a period of twenty years.

Since you already are well aware of the elements of voice you put into stress—wrong pitch, inappropriate timing, shallow breathing, excessive intensity—you can observe their interaction when you use one of these "winging it through" approaches. Be sure to talk aloud to yourself as you work out these suggestions. When you are particularly annoyed with someone, ask yourself what trait the person has that is most irritating. Picture that trait as part of yourself. Decide how you would handle it in yourself. Pretend that you say to that person, "Thank you for being my mirror and showing me where I create stress."

When you are so upset with another person that you can't talk to him or her, pretend he or she is a large pillow you've put in a chair opposite you. Ask him or her twenty questions and say aloud what you think the answer would be after each query. If you don't like an answer, pound your pillow person. If you do, hug him. Take the pillow to bed with you and hug it all night long. The blown-up stress from not being able to talk to someone when *you* had too much to say will have deflated like a balloon by morning.

Don't elevate any human being to a position of divinity, purity, or wonderfulness. If they're in a body, they're working on their problems the same as you are. You are setting yourself up for disappointment every time you expect perfection in any human being, especially people such as ministers, teachers, and doctors. WE ARE ALL HUMAN! Put up a sign that says, "I am never disappointed in anybody." If you are, your expectations and understanding of them need drastic overhauling. In addition, placing these expectations on others creates a constant tension in the relationship. Disappointment, like remorse, guilt, shame, and grief, is an unrelenting generator of stress.

Remember to think of the whole person when someone annoys you. Usually the bad behaviors are the easiest to identify first, but this is only a small part of the total picture. You are overreacting to a segment of a whole human being. After listing all of the good points—if you can't think of any, you haven't completed your research—it is fairly easy to see how the picture or personality is balanced. Often the traits that are most irritating have a positive value if guided. When positively developed, bossiness is leadership, an ability much in demand. Nosiness for the purpose of obtaining juicy morsels for gossip is actually the skill of getting information, the basis for a social worker, counselor, or employment interviewer. Pickiness is care with details that often can make or break the success of a project. With the complete set of traits in front of you, make the choice of putting the positive side of the trait into the foreground and relegating its frustrating counterpart to the background. Loyal, helpful friends have all of these so-called bad traits but, because you have automatically integrated your picture of them, you are comfortable with them. Choose to give others the same consideration, and you choose less stress for yourself. Create opportunities for the person to channel a trait toward positive, helpful use, and you'll both gain.

If you care for someone, particularly if it's a person who cannot respond to a demonstration of caring, take the risk of saying "I love you." Communication of genuine feelings of warmth releases those healing syntoxic hormones that are effective in shutting off your alarm system for stress. Believe me, the stress from not saying "I love you" is worse than it is from saying it and hearing a curt, "Well I don't love you" in reply. In fact, if you did receive that response, you would smile with the realization and relief that the problem wasn't totally yours after all. Until you learn to say "I love you" easily and feel love, give gifts to those you care for and to those you don't. Saying "I love you" is a beautiful gift of yourself, but other kinds of little gifts are just as much part of you. Many of the most thoughtful gifts didn't cost a dime, but do cost time.

Do something sweet, kind, or good for someone every day without telling anyone. If you tell, you've taken your reward. If the person finds out, or catches you, do something even better and don't be caught. Not only will you appreciate your own worthiness more, but you will also feel how good it is to love other people by putting it into practice through giving.

If you are too fearful of "I love you" and too bound to traditional excuses to give (debts, holidays, apologies, and birthdays), then start by admitting to yourself every day that you want love and trying to admit it to at least one other acquaintance. Since love must become a behavior before an attitude will change, find three people to love. (Never just one in the beginning, or that person will become the target for all of your garbage behavior as well as the good!) Deepening relationships with acquaintances is the easiest route. Basically, love means willingness to share time with someone who is sharing back. Usually the sharing is not equal and that makes the opportunity even more challenging.

Start loving yourself by refusing to put yourself down in any way with words ("I'm always a little nervous," "I'm confused," "I'm so clumsy"). Stop belittling others with put-downs even in fun (silly goose, dum-dum, monster, blockhead, dopey). Often these put-downs are just another projection of a part of you that you don't like. Accept any compliment with delight and without adjusting its size. False humility, like false modesty, plus putting yourself down are defensive reactions. They are part of being constantly on guard, and your body will get the real message.

According to the new left-right brain research, the left side is the logical part, the right side the intuitive, and they're always in conflict. They function totally differently. The practical, competitive, decision-making, language-oriented left hemisphere is the male part that is primarily applauded in our culture. One technique to get in touch with the loving, sensitive, holistic, right hemispheric, female part is to learn to see pictures in your mind. Close your eyes and picture exactly what you want to look like, see yourself accomplishing some goal, or watch yourself performing some intricate task well. Next, picture any baby animal that appeals to you, and imagine that it talks and answers clearly and kindly any questions you have. Let it advise you on actions you are considering. Remember that the wisdom accessible from the right brain transcends the logic and problem-seeking needs of the left brain and is likely to be attuned to the fulfillment of your best nature.

Often, choices are made by automatic sensing. Using your right brain intuition can get you back to the basics of sensing. Teach yourself to stop thinking by learning a meditation technique and practicing it fifteen minutes a day. Thought processes can label and reinforce problems through daily rehearsals and keep you from attempting the things you want to do, such as getting well, or being happy, or experiencing nature and feeling loved and valued. In a balanced, successful life, you need all of those possibilities.

A simple meditation technique is to gaze at a lighted candle for a minute and then close your eyes. You will retain an image of the flame. Hold it as long as possible, noting colors, movement, size, shape, and beauty. Repeat the process and see if you can hold the image longer. Another technique is to sit in a relaxed position, eyelids lowered so that only a tiny line of vision is possible. Listen to music by Brahms, Beethoven, or Bach and let your mind flow with the music. Humming with it will prevent thoughts or sleep from overpowering the need for meditation. A third technique is to choose "oh," "ah," "ooo," or any sound, and prolong it while sitting or lying in a relaxed position with eyes closed. Follow the sound, feeling it float into various parts of the head, guiding it down the throat into the chest and back up into the nose and mouth. Repeat the process several times using different sounds, or combining them. Yogis start with an "oh" and let it resolve into an "mmm." "Amen" originated from the chant beginning with "ah" and ending with an "mmm" sound. More complex styles of meditation are described in popular literature and often are discouraging to the beginner who needs a simple, direct approach to stilling the thought process so that later guidance can be obtained from the right brain's intuitive nature. Being able to retain a state of silence in which no thought intrudes may be difficult for the beginner. The benefits from directing your consciousness through the simple techniques described is a daily fifteen-minute gift to yourself and will take you far down the road to balanced use of right and left brain potential. This is part of stress management.

The easiest and most documented technique for managing stress has been around for years and is enjoying a modified comeback under many new names. It's called the autogenic technique and was first used in Germany by J. H. Schultz, a psychiatrist and neurologist, in the twenties. It probably originated from research on sleep and hypnosis carried out from 1890 to 1900 at the Berlin institute of the renowned brain physiologist Oskar Vogt. Vogt developed a series of exercises for his patients he called prophylactic rest-autohypnoses and said that self-directed mental exercises had reduced the stress or its effects and enhanced the overall efficiency of the patient. Shultz carefully questioned patients about the sensations they felt and discovered most of them felt pleasantly heavy and warm. He therefore developed a group of consecutive statements the patients could say to themselves to cause this state. Heaviness and warmth add up to a total relaxation.

The following exercises can help you learn to relax to the point of eliminating the effect of stress. It requires great discipline to practice them daily for six months so that they have the best chance to succeed. However, there is no replacement for taking responsibility for an active role in any therapy. Instead of depending on others, you and your body win over the accumulated daily stress that could eventually kill you. The exercises are effective physiologically even if you are among the 10 percent who never experience the heavy, warm feeling.

In more than fifty studies done over a period of thirty-five years by American, French, Polish, as well as the originating German scientists, autogenic training has proved effective for conditions as different as asthma and chronic depression. Versions of these exercises in "progressive relaxation" are available on cassette tapes in educational catalogs from holistic health organizations and companies who deal in self-help products. My adaptation was developed from a class at the University of California. My clients tape their own sessions to take home for practice.

Here's my routine: Sit in a comfortable chair and rest your arms on its arms. (Don't lie down, or you'll go to sleep before finishing the series.) Lift your right arm slightly off the chair arm. Say, "My right arm is heavy."

(Use left arm if left-handed.) Repeat it twenty-five times, slowly and quietly. Lay it down. Then go to the opposite hand and repeat the same sentence, raising that arm just an inch or two off the chair. Then repeat. "My right leg is heavy," the same number of times or for about two minutes while raising the right leg an inch or two off the floor. Follow the same procedure with the left leg. (Raising the arm and leg was not part of Schultz's procedure; I found it aided concentration on that part, and the actual feeling of heaviness from having the arm raised was a great help in later imagining heaviness without actually raising arm or leg.) Go back to the right arm. Say, "My right arm is warm." Repeat twenty-five times slowly, or for two minutes. Go to the left arm, repeat the phrase. Next to the right leg and then the left leg, keep on repeating regardless of how drowsy you feel.

Now repeat, "My heartbeat is calm and even," again about twenty-five times. "I breathe deeply," is the next series and you will feel it happen. The abdominal area is next and you say, "My stomach is relaxed," and if you're still awake, it probably is! The last statement is "My forehead is cool." Repeat it for two minutes and you've completed about fifteen minutes of concentration. Stretch. Take a deep breath, squeeze your eyelids open and closed several times, shake your shoulders, wiggle your hips, squeeze your fingers and toes, wrinkle your nose, and get a drink of water. You may feel so relaxed that only sleep satisfies, but I always try to accomplish something because I usually can do it much more effectively than before the autogenic exercise. The patience and persistence of autogenic work may be more than you have developed at this point.

234

You might want to try a less demanding variety.

Begin by taking three very deep and complete breaths. Say, "I am relaxed, I feel relaxed," and simply name every part of your body you can think of, from the tip of your head to your little toe, as "my face is relaxed, my face feels relaxed." Some people obtain total body effects by just concentrating on the mouth area—jaws, lips, gums, tongue, palate, cheek. Lightly touching the part of the body you want to relax is helpful to those who learn best by touch. Those who learn by creating images need to picture in their mind each area becoming loose and limp and lazy. Picturing was a technique that I found was frequently mentioned by professional singers to obtain the results they wanted.

Singers, of course, are different from the average voice user. They are voice athletes. Just as the professional swimmer must maintain a rigorous training program to develop coordination of certain muscle groups, so must the singer gradually build up muscle groups. Swimmers must keep their total bodies in excellent condition or they cannot expect top speed and smooth coordination. The same is true for the singers. The care of the entire body is of utmost concern in order that the delicate throat and mouth muscles will produce fine nuances of tone, which require precision timing and perfect control.

I asked singers and their physicians for their advice on avoiding voice stress. They definitely agreed the singer should refuse to sing with inflamed vocal tissues. It is much more difficult to remedy misuse of delicate vocal tissue than to correct sore, overworked, arm and leg muscles. Horror stories abound of singers permanently losing their clear quality after singing in a demanding performance with inflamed vocal tissue. No amount of money and acclaim can compensate for the loss of a career or a life from hemorrhaged vocal folds (the cause of Caruso's death).

As a speech pathologist, I would say the same thing about talking when you have laryngitis. Hang a sign around your neck that says "On Medical Voice Rest" and answer all questions by note. Most people try to whisper and exert even more effort in the whisper to make themselves understood than in normal speaking. Necks and faces strain and contort in the extreme effort. The vocal tissue isn't resting, and it must rest to recuperate. Speech specialists are the only people I've ever known who understood how to do a relaxed whisper, and could consistently do it in spite of continued demands to speak. Don't put stress on your body, and other people too, by your raspy, wrenching whisper.

Another warning for singers from the physicians was to be aware of how they speak. They discussed the plight of Beverly Sills, a well-known opera star who speaks in a range much lower than her singing voice. After a performance she speaks in her correct, natural pitch which is also in a pleasant, high range. Then her voice gradually drops to a level far too low and problems in maintaining clear quality begin. She has had repeated voice difficulties. Lynn Stradley, professional singer as well as professor of voice at Sacramento State University, shared his awakening to the singer's need for care in speaking. "As a lecturer at Florida State University, I found my voice was twice as tired after a lecture as it was from a couple of hours of singing. I realized I was not breathing properly nor using other good vocal techniques that were second nature when I was performing. I worked to retrain myself to move around and use the same skills in lecturing that I had mastered in singing. If you feel any pain or strain, whether speaking or singing, you know you aren't doing something right, and you had better take steps to correct the situation."

If you feel tightening in the throat and chest, are tired after talking for an hour or so, or find yourself coughing or clearing your throat, your body is signaling that you're off your natural voice target. Do something about it right then. Moving around will immediately discourage much of the tension buildup. Sneaking quick deep breaths to clear out the accumulation of gases in the lungs is the next step. Continue to speak but consciously pull your stomach in and push it out as you breathe. You'll need to slow down your speech to do this, and slowing down decreases tension. Next, open your mouth a little wider and let the sound float out. Lower your volume, even if you haven't been talking loudly. Decreasing loudness just a little bit will let your vocal folds start toward recovery. Now gently suck in your cheeks and soothe your drying folds with some lubrication. Drink a glass of water. Stress and dehydration go together, and if you have a long stretch of speaking ahead, a glass of prevention is worth eight ounces of cure! To continue with your recovery process, squeeze your eyes closed and then stretch them open widely. This usually clears the mucus accumulation and allows you to swallow it. If you are speaking publicly, glance down at books and papers while you're squeezing your eyes and no one will be aware of your recovery strategy. If I'm seated at a table, I'll pretend to think, resting my finger tips on my forehead to cover my eye-squeezing, mucus relieving, tension intervention. The friend who taught me these steps condensed the process into "think, move, breathe, suck, squeeze." Even if you're never in a public speaking situation, you probably are occasionally in situations where you feel tension mounting. When your face feels warm and you begin to perspire, the procedure is just as relevant. When your body signals tension, answer it.

Here are some of the other suggestions from the voice professionals for those of you who speak or sing professionally.

1. Avoid eating nuts before talking or singing publicly. Particles of nuts have a way of appearing in the throat at the wrong time and causing havoc.

2. Avoid milk, ice cream, yogurt, or similar products starting at least the day before singing. Singers feel these products stimulated excessive mucus.

3. Avoid eating anything that produces an allergic reaction in the total body. If you want a tone as clear and perfect as possible, the whole body must be balanced. Several singers have temporarily given up chocolate, because it caused a total body reaction, including an outbreak of acne.

4. Antihistamines and aspirin should be avoided because they dry the throat. Aspirin thins the blood and consistent intake of aspirin-containing medicines combined with extensive use of the voice has been known to cause hemorrhaging of the vocal folds.

5. Avoid air conditioning. It dries the air too much.

Singers say it is important to constantly monitor the hydration level of the body, particularly in the summer. A crude but simple test is to observe the urine color. It's always best to "pass pale" since this indicates a good level of hydration.

6. When a dry throat does occur, gargle with a saline solution of one teaspoon salt to one quart of water.

7. Although one well-known singer swears by a can of beer before her performance, other singers and physicians say that any liquor can easily become a psychological crutch. One points out that alcohol constricts the blood vessels in the vocal tissue and that after even a small amount, voice control is lessened.

8. Comfrey tea, an herbal tea, was described as helpful in obtaining relief from allergies. A physician reports that one of the singers he had seen frequently for allergy control no longer required his help after developing the comfrey tea habit.

9. Large amounts of vitamin C can dry out the vocal folds and require careful monitoring if you're singing regularly.

10. The numerous impurities in marijuana are harmful to the vocal tissue. Since it is sold by weight, there is no quality control. Smoking anything dries the throat and constricts the blood vessels. No one who is serious about a vocal career would ever smoke, all of the singers interviewed say emphatically, and the physicians agree.

11. Vocal muscles must be kept in condition by exercises every day. A daily workout beginning with a slow warming up was described by all of the professional singers. Robert White, tenor, warms

up using his arms, legs, and total body by softly going up and down scales and gradually increasing his volume in a liver-shaking crescendo. As part of her daily routine, Ruth Onstatt, soprano, sings a series of five "vowel shapes" on one note and then on many series of five consecutive notes across the keyboard. Lynn Stradley, baritone, sings a group of "yah yah nah nahs" to stimulate jaw movement, a series of "eee's" to encourage placement of tones in the frontal area, and "nee nahs" descending from middle C and going up again for flexibility and control.

12. Avoid parties following a performance. Continuous talking to hundreds of people in a smoke-filled room after an hour or more of singing can be disastrous to the singer's voice. The temptation to drink blood-vessel-constricting champagne at a time when you and your delicate vocal instrument are tired is another reason to skip these celebrations hosted by well-meaning friends. The physicians say that the effects of "after parties" are often worse than a disease's.

13. Taking hormones must be carefully monitored by a physician because the elasticity of the vocal folds may be affected. One physician reported that a young soprano who gradually had lost the ability to execute the two top notes of her range recovered the lost notes when hormone treatment was initiated. She had prematurely suffered a decrease in feminine hormone production, which had caused the reduction in her range. Other singers reported a reduction in range because of the water retention when they began taking birth control pills.

Physicians Friedrich Brodnitz, Wilbur Gould, and Hans Von Leden, who have been extensively involved in treating singers as well as originating research on the singing voice, agree that singing in choirs is a poor practice for a singer who plans a career as a soloist. Research has shown professional singers do not monitor their voices well in choruses and lose track of their vocal effort, thus putting their voices in danger. Nonprofessional singers in the studies tend to ignore the accompaniment and continue to sing with approximately the same amount of loudness. The professional singers increase an average of three decibels for every thirty decibels of increase in the accompaniment, and expend twice the power usually used in singing. Many barbershop quartets become worse instead of better as the years progress. The members sing too intensely to try to balance the total effect of the group. The quality of all of the voices deteriorates from the forcing. Some aged former quartet members have chronic vocal fatigue—the tired voice syndrome.

Many well-known singers have developed growths on their vocal folds. Both Enrico Caruso and Frank Sinatra had growths removed midway through their careers. Although Bing Crosby had a vocal nodule, he chose not to have it removed, and is reported to have said to the laryngologist who discovered it. "Don't you dare touch it, that's my livelihood!"

Indeed, nodules can produce an unusual quality since they add weight to the vocal tissue, but most people do not want the harsh grating sound. Fortunately surgery is not the treatment preferred by laryngologists. They insist that first, a voice analysis must pinpoint what is wrong with the voice; second, adequate speech therapy must be done to correct the voice problem; and third, the patient must thoroughly understand the situation and make a genuine attempt to correct faulty use of the whole mechanism. Only if the nodule persists after all of these conditions have been met, and the patient *is not* a singer, will surgery then be considered. No matter how much skill is used or how little the reaction to the surgery, there will be some fibrosis and scarring at the site of the surgery that will impair a singer's voice. It may be a very minimal change to the ordinary voice user, even a professional actor, but a singer would experience a difference because that fold would not vibrate normally.

It is often up to singers and actors to relay the best current practices of voice specialists to their physicians. Many times, a singer or actor will have to objectively assist a physician unfamiliar with the best current practices recommended by the outstanding medical voice specialists. A general physician treats few patients for voice problems, and probably has neither the time nor the knowledge to devise an individual treatment plan for a professional singer or actor. When miles from a specialist, a singer may experience the first signs of a voice problem. Many singers create disaster by trying everything in the medicine cabinet or taking huge amounts of so-called health foods or vitamin C. If you are a singer, you have felt this panic that arises when no one else can detect a change you feel in your voice. It is up to singers and actors to gain a thorough understanding of their physical limits and the emotions that can trigger voice problems.

One place the outstanding specialists exchange medical advice is at conferences. For example, each year the Voice Foundation brings together professionals from many fields to promote understanding of the dynamics of voice and encourage effective care of the professional voice. Scientists, laryngologists, surgeons, speech pathologists, and music and drama teachers share information at these symposiums.

Unfortunately, much of this information never reaches the very people it could help. If you enjoy singing, are in the midst of preparing for a career in singing, know someone who is, or would just like to know more about the concerns of voice athletes, you will be intrigued by these topics, which were examined at Voice Foundation conferences held at the Juilliard School of Music in 1979.

Many unusual structure differences in the larynx and other areas related to voice production have no noticeable effect on the vocal abilities of singers. Scientists investigated many unique structures, including unusually placed folds, missing uvulas, and strangely positioned epiglottises, and found them to be no cause for surgery or worry for singers or their teachers.

The color of the vocal folds can suggest the appropriate classification of the voice. "Rose-pink, slipper-satin" colored folds are typical of lower voices, while whiter-appearing folds indicate upper register singers. When laryngologists provided this information and data on the length of the folds and size of the entire vocal tract to teachers, they began reclassifying singing students in the early stages of training and adjusted their techniques to meet the needs of the expanded ranges. Singers who thought their limitation was in the baritone or mezzo range were surprised to learn their vocal folds had further potential for training.

Responding to singers' concerns about their overabundance of mucus, the physicians explained that the normal nose manufactures as much as a quart and a half of mucus in 24 hours. Air conditioning, allergens, infections, and stage fright can trigger sudden changes in the amount and kind of mucus produced. The solution is not to eliminate mucus but to stimulate a thinner, less viscous, more watery type. There are products available at drugstores to help with this problem.

When singing where climates are extremely hot or cold, singers were advised to use humidifiers. Vocal folds and noses may not adjust quickly enough when the heating system or humidity differs from the usual, and sudden vocal problems could ensue.

Deviated septums (blockages in the nasal tract) influence breathing, coordination, and lessen lung functioning. A boxer's dramatic improvement in agility after correction of a mangled nose supports the evidence that improved respiration enhances one's total body performance. If breathing is impaired by a deviated septum, surgery is the recommended solution. A singer should consider this during early training while patterns are flexible.

When surgery in the vocal area is unavoidable for a singer, it is important that the anesthetist as well as the surgeon is aware that the patient is a singer. Extra caution should be taken in selecting and placing surgical tubes to avoid as much damage as possible to the delicate vocal tissue.

"How soon will I be able to sing again?" is the first question singers with severe laryngitis ask. Since a variety of germs cause the problem and each person's resistance to particular germs varies, the answer is not simple. Some germs cause very little swelling and others cause prolonged swelling by also affecting the sinus lining. Since laryngitis caused by infection can occur just as suddenly as that caused by overuse, the singer should seek expert consultation as quickly as possible to limit the infectious damage to the cells of the vocal tract. The more damage, the longer the period that the voice rest must be enforced.

You cannot tell the condition of your vocal folds by looking at your throat. Their position in the throat makes it impossible to see them directly. A tiny mirror and sometimes a microscope must be used to indirectly reflect tissue changes and minute tears. One distinguished teacher and singer, Manuel Garcia, made a device to see his own vocal folds and is credited with discovering the technique for indirect laryngoscopy in the nineteenth century. Most singers would find Garcia's feat hazardous and would need expert counsel to interpret what they saw.

Medicine cannot meet all the needs of the sick performer. Vitamins (particularly the B-complex), minerals, and diet need careful planning to insure the fastest recovery possible. No cell in the body can convert sugar into energy without the action of the B vitamins, while zinc and magnesium are especially important in the healing of injured cells. Although many new antibiotics, hormones, enzymes, and drugs are often prescribed, singers should also take the initiative in seeking advice about needed dietary controls and supplements that would be a sensible part of careful health management.

Many singers feel they go overboard in being concerned about their voices, and are usually embarrassed, apologetic, and hesitant about calling doctors. There is, however, no evidence to support their belief that they are hypochondriacs. Only one singer in ninety who visited laryngologists in two widely separated states was eventually described as consistently anxious about ungrounded illnesses. Training insures that singers will be acutely sensitive to the way their voices feel and alert to changes that are imperceptible to others.

Whether or not you make your living with your voice, stopping vocal misuse before it becomes vocal abuse is part of your responsibility to your body. Learning to manage stress during positive or negative situations will extend your life as well as insure that your voice will remain healthy. One other responsibility is guiding children toward understanding the potential they have through their voices and teaching them to care for and monitor voice power in every age of its development. The final chapter will help you to understand the source of voice problems you may now have and provide the groundwork for preventing a replay.

TWELVE

Responsibly Guiding Children's Voices

Voice patterns have their roots in infancy. Even babies show wide differences in the way they cry. It's as though they each attended a different acting school. Some are much louder than others. Breath catching, voice breaks, and gravelly quality are surprisingly frequent, and some even manage frightening choking sounds. Researchers comment that you can hear the whole gamut of human suffering in the primitive cries — everything from pitiful complaints to full blasts of anger and aggression. Unfortunately, often mothers who are unhappy or anxious also have to cope with the babies with the most incredible endurance for loud crying and who also have the most frequent cases of hoarseness.

Of course, we know that allergies run in families and are sometimes part of the reason for the screaming and hoarseness. It is understandably unpleasant to have an overabundance of mucus trickling down the throat when you're new at breathing and swallowing. It can be downright frightening to choke on it, have it go the wrong way, and be ignored so you won't be spoiled.

In a recent conversation, Daniel Boone, recognized voice scientist and author of a text on voice disorders, told me that by the age of nineteen or twenty months, children have learned a voice communication style to control the world around them. Like a primitive people without words, they call by voice alone, ask by voice, love and hate through intonation. Infants start vocally free of inhibition and prohibitions, but quickly learn from the adults around them. Boone told me there is a "pragmatics of voice" just as there is a pragmatics for language. All those little nuances of expression, hidden gestures and looks are discriminating pragmatics that mean far more than the actual words used. Variations in sound, pitch, timing, and intonation function in the same way for voice and are used at a very early age.

Whether you're aware of it or not, you teach your children this voice power value from the time they are tiny infants. By the time they are two-years-old, they have already learned how to embarrass you in a restaurant with their voices. While eating in a Chinese restaurant once, I noticed a two-year-old and a four-year-old expressing their unfamiliarity with oriental cooking as a noodle whizzed past my ear. The parents threatened, cajoled, pleaded, bribed, and promised the children McDonalds later, if they would just be quiet. I could hear varieties of the parents' inflections in the children's voices. Eager to escape the increasing noise level, I opened my fortune cookie and laughed. It read, "Children need models more than critics."

It was my cookie so I decided to test the oriental wisdom. I began a conversation with the children about birthdays, Santa Claue, and grandmas, known to be the going fad with most noodle hurlers in that age group. I was careful that my voice did not communicate criticism or any of the other options the parents had tried. I did not ask questions or put them on the spot as most well-meaning adults do when they meet young children. I did not stare directly into their faces or come too close too quickly. I did not talk to the parents at the same time I was talking to them, nor did I glance at the parents for approval or response. To do either could have quickly lined me up on the wrong side, besides being rude to the very human beings I was talking to. These are all simple courtesies we easily extend to other adults. Without any recognition of the child's uneasiness about our size and our skills, we pompously question them and look to the parents for the answers. Usually the kids live through it and probably learn from it all the things we now can't appreciate. I tried to keep the conversation relaxed, making leading statements that left room for the children to express their feelings without putting them on the spot.

As a result of our conversation, the children calmed down. It is my feeling that as adults we all have responsibility for every child we come in contact with, no matter whose it is or what the situation. Every time you set a model of communication that doesn't require violence, and allows the other person, no matter how small, equal rights and dignity, you build a better life for yourself and for those you touch. Translated into practical ideas, remember hurling accusations invites loud replies and lies (for all ages). With young children, don't talk about an upsetting subject until they are calmer and aren't in the firing line. (I didn't tell them how much I love Chinese food or ask if they enjoyed their dinner.) When they're away from the restaurant and at their own table, you can demonstrate the correct courteous voice to use when eating out and don't like what is served. Maybe it's, "I'm sorry I can't finish this; I ate too much salad and am too full," or just, "No, thank you." Teaching a quiet-voiced courteous "no, thank you," without any supplementary remarks is hard, particularly if there's an adult in your family who always lets you know what doesn't taste right, but seldom compliments anything. Sometimes "no, thank you" isn't sufficient armory and the child is served anyway. Think of alternatives that will help the situation and save you the loud, embarrassing voice power that my son gave me after one of those "no, thank you" bombs.

Course after course of an elegant dinner had been brought to us. Each time my five-year-old son looked at the waitress and said with gusto, "No, thank you." The dish was plopped in front of him anyway as it was for all the other people in the dinner party. After the fourth or fifth "No, thank you," he loudly wailed, "Mom, 'No, thank you' doesn't work here!" Seeing tears in his eyes, I said, "I'm glad it didn't. I'm hungry enough to eat yours too. Why don't you go to the bathroom and I'll trade plates with you." Off he ran, glad to hide his embarrassed tears. Back in time for the dessert—ice cream, in a dish surrounded by red crushed ice—"Ice cream with blood?" he asked. "Just colored ice," I said, wishing he'd have stuck to "No, thank you." He didn't touch it, but did take the lemon that came after the meal, squeezed it into his water and said, "Mmm, I'm sure glad they let you make your own lemonade."

With children, exciting public situations are usually not the place to teach anything, particularly voice habits! The excitement of the situation may become associated with the behavior and you'll get a repeat of something you thought you had corrected with all your might and main. Be careful of using loudness, intensity, and the intonations of sarcasm, anger and hostility, if you don't want to teach the voice inflections you're trying to correct.

If you find that you are already faced with vocal habits that are unpleasant in your child, you still have some alternatives.

It may be the hardest thing in the world to admit you have a problem and need the help of a child to correct it, but that's exactly what will help. Say to your child, "I know I often talk too loudly and crossly. It doesn't help you to do what I want and I end up feeling strained and unhappy and get lots of lines in my face too. How about talking to me in a whisper whenever I do it, and it'll be our secret signal that I'm not using my voice right. Now let's see, what would be all right for *me* to do when you're yelling at the top of your lungs at your dog or your brothers? How about blowing a whistle, ringing a bell, or stamping my feet?"

Usually something can be devised that's known to just the child and you. Children up to twelve like the idea of secret signals and messages that elevate their feelings of importance. Be sure to keep their confidence.

Teaching children not to yell at you when you have yelled a great deal at them is a gigantic task. But if you're willing to change your behavior, he may change his. A "noise" is a better substitute for the yelling. A horn to toot, a bell to ring, a whistle to blow, or chimes to summon you can go a long way to improving your relationship. Much antagonism between parents and children is nailed in by voice.

But what about the whiner? It's not the loudness that's the irritation, it's the continuity, persistence, and nasality. Usually whining develops when children do not get immediate attention or action for some basic need. They keep repeating the request half-crying, half-hoping to get you to act. "Stop your whining," won't work. Ignoring it won't either. Just hearing themselves is pleasurable enough to keep it going. From basic needs, the whining transfers over to all kinds of desires from candy to a pony ride. In fact, whenever they want anything, it becomes an occasion for whining.

Later on, the whining becomes the repetitive demand designed to wear you down. "Please let me go, please let me go. I'll come back on time, I'll . . ." Better to get your voice power strategy straightened out at age three than to endure the persistence of a nine-year-old. Say to the child when everyone is fairly relaxed, "I didn't like the way you asked for the cookie this morning. This is the way you sounded." Imitate. "That annoyed me. Try asking me now in your good voice for one of the brownies I just happen to have in the refrigerator." To sum it up, you didn't dwell on the criticism, you set a model with your voice, you gave the opportunity to practice, and you hooked it up with a reward you know is liked. Remember to praise the cheerful voice the next time something is asked for.

But how can you help the older child who makes repetitive demands in a strong, insistent voice? The demand pattern is like a broken record. It's self-reinforcing. The new rule to give children is that requests must be written out complete with reasons for wanting it. Tell them you'll answer every request with "approved," "not approved," "postponed," or "only if certain conditions are met." At the bottom they are free to write anything in response to your answer. As long as it's written, there's no penalty. Any shouting or screaming will result in the loss of all privileges for a week.

Putting the demand in writing helps them to organize their thoughts, is calming, and starts a habit that will benefit them the rest of their life called "keeping your foot out of your mouth." Spelling, grammar, and legibility are not important to your personal communication. The objective is to reduce the talk and encourage thinking. Most children with inappropriate voices do a lot of strained, stressed talking. Writing immediately takes away the situation in which much of the stress habit occurs. Talking it out usually results in both parties being worn out, tensed up, and beaten down, and it rarely solves the problem of the demanding child. As a matter of fact, it often reinforces it because usually both people continue their demands in the "talking it out," unless they have someone skilled in directing the discussion. Usually the third party to any family discussion says, "All right, I don't want to hear another word, go to your room," or some variation of the administrative intervention to protect their own sanity. Try to avoid the intervention of a third party when dealing with children. Sure both parents can gang up on them and win for the time being, but in the long run you both lose, because you did nothing to interfere with his pattern of using voice inappropriately for power demands.

Power demands are less obvious with other children. Most children who have allergic attacks and asthma receive a great deal of sympathy and attention. A dominant, devoted mom can precipitate a feeling of being overwhelmed and oppressed even in an infant. The feeling of oppression can take the form of difficulty in breathing. Psychiatrists back up the idea that something is wrong in the give-and-take relationships of the asthmatic child. They note that their asthmatic adult patients are not capable of adequate communication in personal contacts. The voice pattern is carried over into adulthood without the child or the parent's awareness that voice contributes to maintenance of the pattern. Shallow breathing, too much or too little nasal resonance, tongue carriage, posture, and the way the voice sounds are habits that keep the body in readiness for the next episode. Change the support system and you begin to change the whole problem.

The breathiness in the voice quality, the wheezing, and other sounds of congestion are familiar in cases of asthma and allergies. When too much mucus is present, raspiness results. The breathing is in the upper chest area and many of the children I have seen have an overly developed upper chest that has probably originated from using these wrong muscles too frequently. Instead of expiring all the air out, they stop and keep their chest rigid in the position for inhalation. It's almost like trying to inhale and exhale at the same time with your chest stuck out! It not only develops an unusual chest contour but a lot of frustration in the muscles trying to respond to the double message:

breathe, don't breathe. This is a very frightening situation to the child and a get-tough attitude won't improve it. These children can feel that both their bodies and their parents are doing them in. They need much help before the attack arrives. They need to be convinced that they can handle it, even when their parents are away.

The next exercise can help create self-confidence. Begin by locating your largest books. Two-pound books are good starters and larger, three-, four-, and five-pound books can be used later. Lie with your child on the floor and place one of the books on each stomach. Practice breathing. Say, "Up, one two three four, down, one two three four," as you inhale and exhale slowly (approximately eight seconds for each cycle). Start with ten complete cycles the first session and then increase by ten until you are doing one hundred — that's only eight minutes of practice. That eight minutes will do much to destroy the panic that accompanies an asthma attack. You've taught the child how to relax, and you have also taught the correct muscles to use in breathing as well as building muscle strength in the correct area for best breathing. The size of the book depends on the size of the child. With adults, I quickly move up to the eight-pound dictionary to increase the muscle action, and then switch to thirteen-pound gym weights.

Of course you wouldn't put books on during an attack. You may lay your hand on the abdomen and say quietly, "I'm going to help you breathe the way we did with the books on your stomach." Evenly and steadily repeat, "Up, one two three four, down, one two three four," and gently raise the abdomen by pushing up with your right hand from underneath. Push down with the left hand resting on top of the abdomen. If you have a timer, set it and tell the children you will do this till the bell goes off. Children, like adults, don't benefit from an indefinite sentence! They need to know the limits. One parent told me he tells the child they will stop when the teakettle whistles. Of course the pot is set at a temperature that will give adequate time. Another uses an egg timer that the child watches. Anything that distracts the child from worrying, or trying to manipulate you, will aid in accomplishing the total relaxation needed to stay in control of the body.

"I control my body," is a phrase I teach in therapy for all of my clients, no matter what the problem. The smallest child learns very quickly how to control parts of the body that can be seen, and it isn't too hard to make the switch over to understanding how to control parts of the body that cannot be seen. When thoroughly convinced of this control, the child is prepared to meet situations when this control will have to be exercised to relieve discomfort. The feeling of asphyxiation is terrifying, no matter what the circumstances, and all children should learn how to handle that possibility and realize that the more they struggle and force, the more likely the choking will become worse. You simply can't explain that to anyone while it is happening.

Children need to know what the vocal folds look like, and you can't see them by looking at the back of your throat. Draw them and show the child how they come together during swallowing. You can also show what happens when a piece of food gets caught or goes down the wrong way toward the lungs, and what must be done to dislodge trapped particles. You can explain how swelling of the throat and folds stops breathing and can cut off the air supply to the body. You can demonstrate the kinds of things that help while you're waiting for medical attention, if the attack is severe enough to warrant that. You don't use a sensational approach and you treat it very much like a mechanic would in talking about fixing a car with a plugged fuel line.

In my experience, children with allergies, sinusitis, and asthma are very talkative and aggressive. They are never soft-spoken, mild-mannered milquetoasts. Maybe we are dealing with a relationship problem and need to teach these children how to get along with others. If you have a lot of problems with people, maybe you may not be the best one to do that teaching. Maybe a grandmother, an aunt or uncle, or close friend can be the model, not the critic, to help the child learn the basics of friendship—giving, receiving, and sharing—with a warm positive feeling.

A good voice model will give some help to the child with the asthmatic, allergic voice, but very direct help will also be needed to show what is being done wrong and how to make it right. I put food coloring and liquid detergent into a five-gallon bottle with about two quarts of water. The child blows through a three-foot-long piece of quarter-inch plastic tubing (from the hardware store) until the bubbles come out over the top of the bottle. Then I put the bottle away. Too much familiarity will soon destroy the novelty.

Show your child a drawing of vocal folds.

This teaches the child to take longer expirations instead of little short ones. By blowing the air completely out, the stomach must be pulled completely in. The right muscle groups for good breathing can then develop. Another energy related benefit is that he'll learn to breathe through the nose instead of the mouth. Be sure to tell the child to keep the lips tight around the tube. Many allergic children become mouth breathers because of frequently stuffed noses. Later on they may become snorers or awaken with hoarse, chronically dry throats from having their mouths wide open all night to breathe. A mouth hanging open, snoring, and an irritating voice quality are not endearing characteristics.

But how do you know whether or not your child is allergic? If the voice has a breathy, hoarse quality in the morning that clears up as the day goes on, an allergy may be the cause. Darkness under the eyes, facial puffiness, and certain other facial and physical characteristics have also been described as allergy symptoms by Dr. Ray Wunderlick, physician, author, and lecturer.

Whether the allergy is recognized, and diagnosis and treatment happen, is up to parents. Some adults discover that their headaches, vocal scratchiness, and nasal stuffiness are caused by allergies they have had since childhood, which were overlooked because they didn't complain. Relief and a dependable voice quality followed treatment. The need for control of allergic reaction before voice improvement techniques can completely succeed is agreed upon by voice specialists. Helping the child into the habit of using the best voice takes some specific help from a parent, as the child probably will never have a concomitant problem to motivate speech therapy.

That may sound like a rough assignment but it really needn't be. It is easy to incorporate vocal exercises in an amusing way into many family activities. For example, when you're playing a card game or other board game, you can add the rule that not only must the players describe each move, but they must hold their nose while doing it. Right away, everyone will become aware of the difference in resonance. No discussion is needed. Another game addition may be to talk like a robot when it is your turn. You must take hold of your jaw and move it up and down as you describe your move or ask for a card. This not only slows down the speech, but projects it out of the mouth and reduces the vocal effect of the allergy.

Playing your family card or board games with everyone using a high squeaky voice or a low grouchy voice will help the child to become aware of the differences in voice quality. The more vocal experimentation that is done, the easier it will be to eliminate the voice pattern of allergy. Using puppets, changing voices for each character, is another activity that can require as little as brown paper bags and crayons to make the character. Later on, one puppet is created to always be the child, and of course this puppet always speaks in the child's clearest best voice, no matter how strangely all the others talk. The secret code to help the children find the best voice is to say, "mmm sss ahh." This helps them feel nasal tension move into relaxed air flow and then into a jaw position that should start them speaking with good quality.

If the child is still a screamer outside of the game situation, then try the best kind of explanation for what can happen from vocal misuse — a demonstration. Show the child a skin callus and talk about what caused it. (The skin protects itself by becoming rougher and thicker where it's overused. Sometimes before the callus develops, a blister appears.) Too much wear on one spot can cause soreness, hard spots, and swollen places on the voice tissue, too. Drawing a picture of the vocal folds (a circle with two lines across the center) and explaining that they are not strong "cords" but very delicate, moist tissue will also help. Show that where the folds come together most strongly and frequently is the very place growths can occur. Draw little bumps facing each other just beyond the first third of each fold. "This causes hoarseness and a funny feeling in your throat. If you start talking in an easy, quiet voice, then they can go away by themselves. If they don't, then the doctor must take them off to keep your voice tissue healthy. Of course you don't want to hurt any part of your body, especially a part that is so important to you! I know you will not shout, yell, and holler when it's not necessary. And if it is necessary, you'll take a big deep breath first."

No one knows how early nodules can develop. Otolaryngologist Frederick Brodnitz and professors of speech pathology D. Kenneth Wilson and William Perkins suggested they may even begin in infancy but may not reach the attention of a physician until some other problem requires a look at the vocal folds. Dr. Wilson recalled an incident of infant twin sisters. One was a screamer. Later she began choking and having difficulty swallowing. An examination revealed the nodules, which were removed. "It turned out that the nodules had nothing to do with the swallowing problem. But if the child hadn't had this problem, we would not have discovered the nodules," Dr. Wilson said.

According to these specialists, about 80 percent of the cases of nodules in children can be eliminated through voice management rather than surgery. Of course as parents of a child who screams, yells, and shouts too frequently, you will want to think about the reasons for the behavior. If you're sure you aren't the voice model, what are other causes for the shouting? Competition with older brothers and sisters? A need to have more attention because the child feels insecure about something (size, intelligence, lack of skills older children have)? Is the child actually a very fearful one who covers scared feelings with boisterousness? Is the child a low achiever trying to make up for it by being tough? Are the child's close friends also loud? What situations in your home seem to cause the worst voice behavior? Maybe these questions will send you scurrying to the library for a book to help you find solutions. There are also courses and cassettes available in Parent Effectiveness Training. Schools often have counseling services available as do many agencies and some churches. Just as there are reasons that keep wrong pitches and loudness habits going in adults, there are reasons for your child's voice habits.

Just as a pearl is found in an ugly oyster, a cure is often found in the symptom. Consider a symptom to be a message. By doing something with the symptom, you may answer every child's hidden message: "I need to feel loved, valued, and protected." Playing the games suggested, having discussions in which the child does

262

the figuring out, asking for the child's advice all reach far beneath the skin. These are concrete demonstrations that you'll take time to share, make him feel stronger, freer, and more capable. The child may no longer need the symptoms to substitute for a lack of secure feelings. If not satisfied in childhood, these feelings can literally grow to runaway proportions during the years to follow.

The teenage years are ones of great physiological and psychological changes. Suddenly their world is turned upside down by strange feelings caused by rapid growth of bones and tissue. The hormones begin to flow and puberty stops all of the delicious nonsense of childhood. More is expected everywhere, and it is difficult to measure up. Things escape out of their mouths that merit swats from loving, compassionate mothers. Dad says, "Shape up or ship out!" The energy level makes them often feel like being in a fast car but not in control of the wheel. Even the major means of communication, voice, can't be depended upon. Is it any wonder that unfortunate voice patterns begin here that cause havoc for a lifetime?

Physicians, voice specialists, voice scientists, and voice teachers all fervently insist that puberty is no time for straining the voice. Yet cheerleading camps, youth choirs, and music written for adult voices with lengthy rehearsals are all offered to keep teenagers out of trouble. In the end, they may prevent them from reaching full voice potential. Even with the very best care, ideal conditions, and superb teachers, not one child who has sung with the Vienna Choir Boys has ever gone on to become a great singer. That's the result of a study of all the children who had sung with them over a period of fifty years. The obvious conclusion reached by the researchers is that the voices were worn out from overuse. Think of the possible tremendous loss in talented singers and in life careers.

It is therefore no wonder that voice specialists caution parents and overzealous music teachers and choir directors not to push at this critical age. Voice scientist Dr. Harry Hollien shared some of the results of a five-year study of boys' voices. He found boys as young as ten and one-half years and as old as sixteen years beginning adolescent voice changes. He said the changes in the vocal tissue could take as long as five and one-half years to complete or as little as one month. You'd almost need some scientific instruments to know when he is experiencing the most change and should not be misusing his voice. Dr. Hollien said the average boy goes through the change at about fourteen and one-half years and completes it in six months. "The average boy" may be a mathematical myth, as is the average girl who begins menstruation and voice change at age twelve and completes it before we notice her deeper tones. Dr. Hollien said that the information about girls' voice changes is still incomplete. We don't really know when they begin and end. Some girls at fifteen and a half were still in the voice change process according to Dr. Hollien. Doesn't it make you wonder what the quality of many girls' voices would be like if they were not screaming, cheering, shouting, and yelling at high school sports events, rock concerts, and talking over the noise of loud stereos?

Some people even think this is good exercise to stretch muscles of a limited range. Not true, according to the scientists who find that during puberty the physiological capability of both boys' and girls' voices is forty-eight semi-tones, ten more than they will have when the voice tissue stops changing. The instability of the growing tissue makes it nearly impossible for them to produce the same highs and lows consistently, and they shouldn't be in situations that force them to try.

Dr. D. Kenneth Wilson, professor of speech pathology at the University of New York, said that it's hard to stop teenagers who want to sing, and that the best parents can do is to find a voice teacher to show them how to do it properly. Part of Dr. Wilson's work is counseling children who have already developed nodules and helping them to learn to take responsibility for their voice behavior.

Most voice changes in adolescence never reach the attention of a speech pathologist. Most kids bungle through it without help. Sometimes peers and parents interfere dramatically with the child's change — and it stops. Suppose the new voice emerging is in the tenor range, perhaps not as acceptable to the young man as the baritone majority. Not liking or trusting the new voice, he hangs on to the previously accepted child's voice. Or maybe he lowers his chin and secretly tries to force his squeaky, unpredictable voice to go down. Both of these reactions can end up causing many serious problems. A parent who suspects the son will be a tenor can start early to explain how rare tenors are and to make sure he knows about the contributions of famous tenors and hears and sees some of the modern and classical tenor voices. Although he may never sing, he can feel the pride of being in the same voice group as the magnificent Luciano Pavarotti, Jose Carerros, and John Vickers. The voices of the popular John

Denver, Elton John, and Neil Sedaka can also be used as examples to help persuade him that tenor is more than okay.

Short vocal folds that are part of being a tenor or a soprano usually occur in boys and girls with a shorter than total build, as well as a short neck. Taller youngsters usually have longer necks, longer vocal folds and, hence, deeper voices. But of course, outside structure is not a completely reliable way of predicting the size of inside structures. Voice scientists say they are still looking for a way to classify voices at an early age so that optimal training is possible, and serious problems can be avoided.

Dr. Brodnitz shared his experiences of helping young men who chose to speak in high voices rather than go their natural, deeper, baritone range. Sometimes the low voice means adding the responsibility of manhood to an adolescent unready for it. In other cases, letting go of the child's voice means letting go of Mama's love and devotion. Only rarely does the retention of a child's voice after puberty mean that male hormones have not been secreted on schedule, Dr. Brodnitz said. If the child is headed towards sixteen and far below his peers in size and other pubic changes, he may need the help of the warmest, most supportive family physician you can find. He needs to hear the hormonal explanation in the right words and to be guided and supported during any needed treatment. Shopping for a doctor for this delicate assignment is the hallmark of courageous parents, who although worried and frightened, should not be controlled by any medical receptionist who claims the doctor is too busy to talk to them about the problem, or who gives commercials for the physician who pays her salary and insists you don't need to meet the doctor before treatment. You tell her that only after you've talked eyeball-to-eyeball will you know if this is the right doctor for this tricky assignment, and that, of course, may include being the one who recommends a caring specialist for your son. In most of the cases I know of, the family practitioner was able to carry out the treatment without adding to the child's anxieties the drama of the expensive specialist. In my personal experience, few hormonal specialists have demonstrated the personality traits I feel would have enabled them to work with teenage problems. The focus of their training is of course on the disorder rather than the art of dealing with the individual who may be very unhappy about the problem as well as feeling strange because he has to see a specialist.

With the increase in all kinds of problems in adolescence, including venereal diseases, pregnancies, starvation, and suicides, a new kind of doctor has emerged, called the phoebetrician. He treats not only the adolescent physical problems but also manages the psychological problems that accompany them. Recognizing the uneven growth patterns cause tremendous worry over normality, the phoebetrician helps smooth the way for the adolescent who may suddenly find himself in an adult body, but with a child's emotions. It may be just as traumatic to remain in a child's body, while all his friends pass him up. Intellectually and socially, he may have matured, but his body still hasn't changed, and his buddies may tease him unmercifully. Many difficulties that parents have with their adolescents actually are more related to how the growing child is getting along with his peers.

Although I have used boys' voices as examples, I have known of several teenaged girls who were developing strange voice habits, but received no support or help from their parents. "She sounds just like Aunt Tillie. It's just part of her, and probably not worth bothering about," or "Well at least with that funny low voice, she won't go unnoticed!" True, many girls mature into women who are undaunted by a poor voice quality, but with modern help available, they should be encouraged to work for the changes that they need to develop their optimal voices. There are always big and little hints that tell you or your child that you might need some professional guidance. Here's a list of complaints that turned out to be signs that help was needed from medical, dental, and/or speech specialists.

1. Frequent bouts of hoarseness. Anything from an audible lack of clarity to a gravelly, rough sound.
2. Habitual throat clearing after a short series of sentences.
3. Coughing unrelated to a cold. Often just a small cough that occurs two or three times in a conversation.
4. Feeling extremely tired after talking (no other activity involved and wanting to rest and not talk at all).
5. Feeling irritation and pain in the area where you produce sound.
6. Feeling pressure or pain in the outer upper chest, just beneath the neck.
7. Swelling of the veins or arteries in the neck.
8. Feeling of extreme stiffness in the neck and shoul-

- der area.

9. Frequent lump-in-the-throat feeling, unrelated to specific people situations.

10. Irritation or tickling in the ear area without actual ear problems.

11. Repeated sore throats or burning sensations in the throat.

11. Frequent scratchy, dry throat.

13. Tenderness in the front and back neck muscles when you gently massage them.

14. A rumble in the chest, tension and tightness in the chest.

15. A stinging sensation in the soft palate.

16. Avoiding conversation because talking requires too much physical effort.

17. A choking sensation and feeling speech is swallowed.

18. A toothache or aching jaws without apparent cause.

19. Frequent backache with neck tension.

20. Frequent headaches with tendency to scowl or frown. May have deep lines across forehead recording this frequent muscle pattern.

21. Too much mucus or too little mucus in the throat area with frequent need to clear throat or cough.

22. Pain at the base of the tongue.

23. Pain in the front or back of the neck.

24. Not being able to sing as high or as low as recently without any sign of infection.

25. Inability to talk at will or at length on varied occasions.

26. Repeated loss of voice.

27. Voice breaks into a higher or lower pitch while

talking.

28. Voice skips certain words and no sound comes out. Suddenly returns as though normal.
29. Voice comes and goes during the day. Sometimes you have only a whisper instead of a full voice.
30. Clear strong voice in the morning; tired, raspy voice in the evening
31. Raspy, tired voice in morning that progressively gets worse during the day.
32. Certain speech sounds consistently missed or slurred.
33. A high-peaked hard palate with an overbite, short upper lip, and a tongue that thrusts forward in swallowing.
34. A clicking sound in the jaws; sometimes jaw seems to slip out of place.
35. Teeth grinding night or day.

Finding appropriate help in some localities for some of the problems is difficult. Many people complain of years of the run-around before they locate the specialist tuned in to their problem. I've found this particularly true of temporo-mandibular joint dysfunction. Recently I referred a voice client to a dentist for what I suspected was the dental distress or temporo-mandibular joint syndrome. Her lips, jaws, and tongue moved in a strange, restricted pattern. She complained of stiffness and cracking noises in her jaw, neck, and back, and said pressure in the bridge of her nose and aches while chewing and swallowing were frequently upsetting. She had been told by her family doctor her pains were just tension and she needed to learn to cope with others better. She was told by an ear, nose, and throat physician that her aches might be related to posture because he could find nothing in her throat, ears, or nose to account for her discomforts. A year with a psychologist had not relieved her aches nor her determination to find out why she had so many strange pains. She interpreted the psychologist's comments about communication to mean she needed speech training and came for an evaluation. I told her to spend her money on getting her jaw situation taken care of and then, if she'd like some voice help to improve her use of voice, she would benefit and enjoy it more.

Dr. Harold Gelb, professor of dentistry at New Jersey College, told voice professionals one-third of our population has jaw problems, and that with corrective treatment both speaking and singing improves. Behavioral, psychological and environmental factors all have to do with the way you use your vocal folds and the mandible plays a major role in this, according to Dr. Gelb's twenty-five years of research and experience. Stress from not having the head of the jawbone where it belongs in its socket will trigger problems throughout the entire body. Since 50 percent of the total nervous output from the brain goes to the jaws, teeth, eyes, ears, and nose, it isn't difficult to see how stress could cause an overload on these nerves. Pain signals from many other parts of the body then confuse the situation and the individual may go from specialist to specialist without ever discovering the back, neck, head, jaw, or leg aches are caused by the temporo-mandibular joint. Dr. Gelb said the problem is easy to identify because the same characteristics are obvious. The right eye-brow is higher than the left, the right eye is larger and higher than the left. The cheekbone on the right is higher, the right ear is higher. The same disparity above the neck exists below the neck: one lower shoulder, lower breast, lower hip, lower knee, and one shorter leg. "When the jaws are in their proper position, every muscle group is like the rock of Gibraltar," said the dental specialist. You lose 25 to 50 percent of your strength when they're not. Some of Dr. Gelb's recent research and treatment was done with the Philadelphia Eagles, with Notre Dame, and several other teams. The improvement was verified by various muscles tests, X-rays, and improved performance.

Resources for further information include the American Equilibration Society, c/o Richard Coy, School of Dental Medicine, South Illinois University, Edwardsville, Illinois, 62025 and the American Academy of Cranio-mandibular Orthopaedics. The secretaries of these groups can refer you to local people for treatment. The expense is considerable but so is the relief.

Many of the symptoms directly related to irritation and pain in the throat should be evaluated by an ear, nose, and throat physician. One physician reported that in thirty-eight patients who had nodules, polyps, or contact ulcers, eleven of them were teeth grinders. A family physician or a dentist might overlook this possible relationship and not do the laryngoscopic examination, a difficult procedure for children. Teeth grinding cannot be done without the neck, throat, tongue, and jaw tension that can affect the vocal folds. Dr. Gelb suggested that the prevalence of teeth grinding among normal people may be eleven out of thirty-eight too. This symptom of stress should be understood in children or adults as a signal of possible more serious underlying difficulties.

Dr. Gelb also felt that the abnormal swallowing pattern (tongue thrust) in which the teeth are out of contact and the tongue is forced between or against the front teeth was also a source of future problems. He stated that, in his experience, well over 50 percent of the tongue-thrusting population developed the cranio-mandibular syndrome with malocclusion. For help with this problem contact the International Association of Oral Myology, c/o R. Barrett, 1645 North Alvernon, Tucson, Arizona 85712, or look under the listing Myofunctional Therapy in the yellow pages of the phone book. The American Speech and Hearing Association, 10801 Rockville Pike, Rockville, Maryland 20852, will assist you in finding a speech pathologist to work with your child if the tongue thrust also involves a distortion of speech sounds.

If a child is having difficulty in learning to talk, professional help may be needed, or you may need some professional advice. Many parents are consoled by a physician or a relative with "She'll outgrow it," or "He's just like Uncle Harry," or "You are an overanxious parent." Remember that the quality of the answer to any question depends upon the knowledge, training, and experience of the person you ask. Many professionals and most relatives will give you answers even though they may not be truly informed about the problem. The parents of nearly every child

273

with problems of articulation and delayed speech that I have treated were told at some time, by someone they trusted, that the child would outgrow it. I have seen some older children who did outgrow a problem, but their self-image was distorted, and they were shy and unsure in simple situations. Some teenagers and adults who end up in my voice improvement class are still outgrowing the problem. Looking down and avoiding direct eye contact, covering the mouth with their hands while speaking, jerky body movements, fidgeting, crossing and uncrossing the arms, and a general reticence to speak spontaneously are a few things I notice among those who say they outgrew childhood speech problems. Some remember parents actively correcting them and still dislike talking to them because of old feelings that they still don't measure up in their parents' eyes. If the child has a speech problem, I suggest parents shop for a specialist they can communicate with also. Changing some old ineffective attitudes they have as parents, which they learned from their own parents, may affect the progress of the child.

No specialist can guarantee results, and the speech pathologist is no exception. There are just too many factors affecting the situation besides the parents. The other members of the family, health, school, and peer relationships, basic personality, as well as the major events in a child's life can all be a help or a hindrance. Divorces; traumatic moves; deaths of relatives, friends, or animals; and critical events in the lives of those close to him can seriously affect the recovery or treatment of any communication problem. For most of my clients, I ask the parents not to criticize or carry out any speech exercise with the child at home. Negative remarks, sarcasm, and pressure to practice all sabotage my work toward helping the child learn that communication is easy, wonderful, joyful, and an adventurous part of life. Better no therapy at home than bad therapy that results in the child's carrying over a defensive attitude toward the speech therapy situation. As you might guess, when it is a financial struggle for the parent to pay for the therapy, they transmit this anxiety to the child, who learns it easily. Working with an anxious child pressured by parents, I can see no hope for the treatment schedule to be shortened! I believe the best help a parent can give during the treatment process is to convince the child that he is strong and capable, no matter how small or incapacitated he may feel, and that he is loved and valued simply because he belongs to them. This is especially true for the child who stutters.

I am convinced that all stuttering has multiple causes and, therefore, that no treatment approach will work for all stutterers. At one time, for the child under six, a counseling approach for parents only was the general method of management. New research has supported the idea that early help can be beneficial to the child who very possibly may be one of the group of stutterers who will have the problem much of their adult life. The National Stuttering Project with its groups throughout the United States is testimony that many, many stuttering adults are troubled by the effect on their lives. Job discrimination and difficulty in social contacts are just two problems the project is active in solving. Membership is open to all and you may obtain more information by writing The National Stuttering Project, 656 Eighth Avenue, San Francisco, California 94118. They have a file of speech pathologists and other therapists and will provide information on other resources as well as where the closest group may be meeting. In any case, if your child is stuttering excessively, no matter how young, get an expert opinion. The American Speech and Hearing Association offers a list of inexpensive, helpful pamphlets about stuttering for parents and the child.

Passing on the joy of relaxed, easy communication, we can all help foster an atmosphere of openness for now and the future. Communication is my life, my business, my hope, my dream for the world. We are all part of the stream of communication. How well we use the natural potential of our voice is a choice we can make at any time. To enhance this beautiful gift of speech by creatively learning to use our voices with all their nuances of splendor offers an unfolding unending adventure into the mainstream of the triumphant synergy of growth among people.

Evelyn Burge Bowling has spent more than twenty years working with children and adults to improve their speaking voices. Currently, she is a speech pathologist and educational consultant at her own clinic, Sunrise Language, Speech, and Educational Services in Citrus Heights, California. She has also worked as a school speech and hearing therapist in hospitals, in remedial clinics, and as a private practitioner. Ms. Bowling received a bachelor's degree in speech and speech pathology from the University of California, and she completed her master's work at California State University. An active professional, she is a member of the American Speech and Hearing Association, California Speech and Hearing Association, California Speech Pathologists and Audiologists in Private Practice, Down's Syndrome Congress, and the California Writers.

Index

THESE ZEBRA MYSTERIES
ARE SURE TO KEEP
YOU GUESSING

TRIVIA MANIA: TV GREATS

TRIVIA MANIA: I LOVE LUCY   (1730, $2.50)

TRIVIA MANIA: THE HONEYMOONERS   (1731, $2.50)

TRIVIA MANIA: STAR TREK   (1732, $2.50)

TRIVIA MANIA: THE DICK VAN
DYKE SHOW   (1733, $2.50)

TRIVIA MANIA: MARY TYLER MOORE   (1734, $2.50)

TRIVIA MANIA: THE ODD COUPLE   (1735, $2.50)